CLOSED™

V O L U M E   3 7

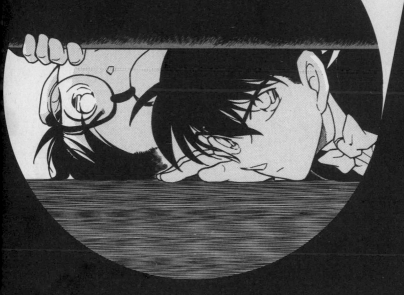

G o s h o   A o y a m a

Case Briefing:

Subject:
Occupation:
Special Skills:
Equipment:

Jimmy Kudo, a.k.a. Conan Edogawa
High School Student/Detective
Analytical thinking and deductive reasoning, Soccer
Bow Tie Voice Transmitter, Super Sneakers,
Homing Glasses, Stretchy Suspenders

The subject is hot on the trail of a pair of suspicious men in black when he is attacked from behind and administered a strange substance which physically transforms him into a first grader. When the subject confides in the eccentric inventor Dr. Agasa, they decide to keep the subject's true identity a secret for the safety of everyone around him. Assuming the new identity of first-grader Conan Edogawa, the subject continues to assist the police force on their most baffling cases. The only problem is that most crime-solving professionals won't take a little kid's advice!

Table of Contents

File 1: Bye-Bye..5
File 2: Richard's Choice (1)......................................23
File 3: Richard's Choice (2)......................................41
File 4: Richard's Choice (3)......................................57
File 5: The Footsteps of Darkness (1)............75
File 6: The Footsteps of Darkness (2)............93
File 7: The Footsteps of Darkness (3)..........109
File 8: White Snow, Black Shadow.................127
File 9: A Dangerous Meeting......................147
File 10: Along for the Ride.........................163

CASE CLOSED

Volume 37
Shonen Sunday Edition

Story and Art by GOSHO AOYAMA

© 1994 Gosho AOYAMA/Shogakukan
All rights reserved.
Original Japanese edition "MEITANTEI CONAN" published by SHOGAKUKAN Inc.

Translation
Tetsuichiro Miyaki

Touch-up & Lettering
Freeman Wong

Cover & Graphic Design
Andrea Rice

Editor
Shaenon K. Garrity

Printed in the U.S.A.

Published by VIZ Media, LLC
P.O. Box 77010
San Francisco, CA 94107

10 9 8 7 6 5 4 3
First printing, January 2011
Third printing, April 2014

I CUT THE FINAL WIRES AND DIS-ABLED THE BOMB.

I CHICKENED OUT.

CONAN!

WAIT!

HEY, DON'T SHAKE THE ELEVATOR! THE BOMB WILL—

WHOA!

THUP

SORRY.

I KNEW THEY'D GET SCARED.

THAT'S OKAY, CONAN. LET'S JUST CONTACT THE RESCUE TEAM AND GET THE HECK OUT OF HERE!

ALL WE'VE GOT IS "EVIT." DON'T SEE HOW THAT CAN LEAD US TO THE NEXT BOMB.

VROOM

BUT THE CLUE—

THEY'LL BELIEVE THE POLICE SACRIFICED HUNDREDS OF LIVES TO SAVE THEIR OWN HIDES!!

PERFECT. THE PUBLIC WILL THINK THE COPS MADE THE KID STOP THE BOMB.

WAH WAH

HUH?

I'M TALKING TO HIM NOW!

AMAZINGLY, THE WORK WAS DONE BY THE YOUNG BOY TRAPPED IN THE ELEVATOR!!

THE BOMB HAS BEEN DEACTIVATED!!

LISTEN TO THOSE CHEERS!!

BUT THE NICE POLICEMEN TOLD ME WHICH WIRES TO CUT! IT WAS EASY!

JIMMY?

YOU BET!

WEREN'T YOU SCARED, LITTLE BOY?

FBBT

HUH?

UM, ACTUALLY...

WE'VE STILL GOT TWO AND A HALF HOURS TO FIND THE SECOND BOMB!

DON'T WORRY ABOUT THAT CLUE!

ER, DETECTIVE SATO...

YEAH, RIGHT.

IT'S FOOLISH TO SACRIFICE YOUR LIFE FOR THE SAKE OF STRANGERS.

YOU MADE THE RIGHT CHOICE.

I'M PROUD TO BE YOUR BOSS!

I KNEW YOU'D DO IT, CONAN!

I'M SO GLAD YOU'RE OKAY!!

HA HA HA...

...THOUGHT THE SAME THING.

I BET THE BOMBER...

DING DONG DING

I WAS JUST WATCHING THOSE *WEIRD TRUCKS* THAT KEEP COMING AND GOING.

VROOM

HUH? OH YEAH.

THE NEXT EXAM'S "COMPRE-HENSION." YOU'RE GOOD AT THAT. YOU'RE ON EDGE. WHAT'S UP?

WHEW... ONE MORE EXAM TO GO.

THE BIG CITY PING-PONG TOURNAMENT'S GONNA BE HELD AT OUR SCHOOL.

THEY'RE PROBABLY MOVING ALL THE PING-PONG TABLES FROM THE BASEMENT STORAGE ROOM TO THE GYM.

THE POLICE WON'T FIND THEM.

HEH HEH HEH...

HAVEN'T YOU BEEN DOWN IN THE STORAGE ROOM? THEY'VE GOT FIVE HUGE OIL DRUMS THERE. IT'S A PAIN IN THE NECK TO GET THE TENNIS NETS OUT...

I HOPE THEY MOVE OUT ALL THOSE OIL DRUMS WHILE THEY'RE AT IT. I HATE THOSE THINGS!

WHAT OIL DRUMS?

FIVE SECONDS LEFT...

EVEN IF THEY DO, IT'S TOO LATE NOW.

ONE ...

TWO ...

FOUR ...

THREE ...

ZERO ...

SORRY, BUT THAT NUMBER IS NO LONGER IN SERVICE.

THE BOMB SQUAD ENTERED THE SCHOOL QUIETLY SO YOU WOULDN'T HEAR THEM THROUGH YOUR WIRETAP...

...AND DIS-MANTLED ALL FIVE OF THE BOMBS HIDDEN IN THOSE OIL DRUMS.

"DON'T BOTHER TRYING TO GET A GOOD CLOSER READY, 'CAUSE AT THE END I'M GOING TO TURN THE GAME AROUND."

I'm a fast-pitching, strong-slugging Major Leaguer. Batter up— let's start the extra innings. The game will start at noon tomorrow and end at 3:00 in the afternoon. Don't bother trying to get a good closer ready, 'cause at the end I'm going to turn the game around.If you want to stop the game, ...and see me,

"I'M A FAST-PITCHING, STRONG-SLUGGING MAJOR LEAGUER. BATTER UP— LET'S START THE EXTRA INNINGS."

YOUR MESSAGE TOLD US EVERY-THING WE NEEDED TO KNOW.

SUR-PRISED THAT WE FIGURED IT OUT?

TAKE THE LETTERS "ERA" OUT OF "EXTRA," AND YOU'RE LEFT WITH "XT"!

SO THE MESSAGE IS, "DON'T BOTHER WITH THE E.R.A."

A GOOD CLOSER IS A PITCHER WITH A GOOD E.R.A.

YOU USED "MAJOR LEAGUER" TO MAKE US THINK IN ENGLISH.

EXTRA–ERA =XT

COMING!

HEY, SATO! WE'RE ON OUR WAY TO VISIT SANTOS AT THE HOSPITAL!

...THAT THE BOMB WAS PLANTED WHERE *SHE* WAS.

AFTER ALL, I COULDN'T STOP WORRYING...

PIP

PIP

PIP

ZZT

PIP

YES

BYE-BYE, MATSU-DA.

I PROMISE I'LL NEVER FORGET YOU.

FILE 2: RICHARD'S CHOICE ①

BWA HA HA!!

THAT WAS PERFECT, MR. MOORE!!

WONDERFUL!!

AND CUT!!

DID HE HAVE TO *WINK* AT THE END?

I'M GLAD YOU LIKED IT!

YOU LOOKED SO COOL, DAD!

PLEASE! FEEL FREE TO CALL ON ME ANY OLD TIME!

YOU'RE A LIFE-SAVER! THE TV STAR WHO USUALLY HOSTS OUR SHOW IS OUT WITH THE FLU!

THE ONLY CHARACTERS IN THIS EPISODE...

THAT'S OUT OF THE QUESTION, DETECTIVE.

ER, THAT'S OKAY!

IN FACT, I COULD EVEN APPEAR IN THIS EPISODE AS A *SPECIAL GUEST STAR*...

I WONDER WHAT'S TAKING MISS UJO SO LONG.

HMPH...

KAZAMI, PLEASE BACK OFF.

LET'S NOT GET INTO A FIGHT BEFORE THE SHOOT!

NOBUHARU NAGUMO (31) THE DAUGHTER'S HUSBAND

THAT'S HER.

I REMEMBER WHEN THEY CALLED HER "JAPAN'S SWEETHEART"! WHAT A HONEY!

MISS UJO? ARE YOU ALKING ABOUT RURI UJO?

SHE'S 37 AND NEVER MARRIED. THAT OLD SPINSTER HAD BETTER NOT PUT THE MOVES ON ME!

"JAPAN'S SWEET-HEART," MY REAR END.

OF COURSE! SHE'S THE ONE WHO SUGGESTED YOU AS THE GUEST HOST FOR THIS EPISODE!

CAN WE MEET HER? PRETTY PLEASE?

NO DANGER OF THAT, KID.

I WOULDN'T GO FOR SOME WET-BEHIND-THE-EARS IDOL...

...WHO'S ALREADY WASHED UP.

RURI UJO (37) THE OLD WIDOW

BUT WE'VE MET BEFORE, RICHIE.

THANK YOU SO MUCH FOR INVITING ME!

NICE TO MEET YOU! I'M RICHARD MOORE!

SHE'S EVEN MORE BEAUTIFUL IN PERSON!

YAHOO!! ♡

DOESN'T THE MOLE UNDER MY LIP RING ANY BELLS?

NO WAY! I'D REMEMBER *YOU*!

YOU'RE...

YOU...

WELL, RICHIE?

YOUR SURNAME'S DIFFERENT, AND YOU USED TO WEAR THOSE POP-BOTTLE GLASSES...

Ruri   Doigaki

I DIDN'T RECOG- NIZE YOU AT ALL!

THEY KNOW EACH OTHER? NO WAY!

NOT SINCE JUNIOR HIGH!

RURI- CHAN? LONG TIME NO SEE!

SO HOW COME YOU'RE STILL ON THE MARKET? I CAN'T BELIEVE *YOU'D* HAVE TROUBLE LANDING A MAN.

YOU BET, BABY!

THINK I LOOK BETTER WITHOUT THEM?

I'VE NEVER MARRIED 'CAUSE I'VE ALWAYS HAD A CRUSH ON *YOU.*

DON'T BE SILLY.

ER, UM, JUST SOME NEIGHBOR- HOOD KID...

AND WHO'S THIS?

PLEASE DON'T JOKE AROUND. HE'LL BELIEVE YOU.

BOOM

SURE. WE WENT TO SCHOOL TOGETHER FROM KINDERGARTEN THROUGH JUNIOR HIGH.

YOU KNOW MY MOM?

OH! ARE YOU EVA'S DAUGHTER?

THE NAME'S RACHEL!

I'M HIS DAUGHTER.

HOW DID THE **SMARTEST GIRL** IN SCHOOL FALL FOR THE **BIGGEST BRAT** IN SCHOOL AND EVEN MARRY HIM?

I STILL DON'T GET IT.

GOOD QUESTION.

THEY HAVEN'T STOPPED FIGHTING YET.

THEY'D GET INTO FIGHTS, AND WE'D ALL JOKE THAT THEY WERE HAVING ANOTHER LOVER'S SPAT!

YOU BET THEY WERE! EVA WAS A REAL ICE PRINCESS MOST OF THE TIME, BUT SHE **LOST IT** WHENEVER SHE TALKED TO RICHIE!

KNOCK IT OFF...

WERE THEY ALREADY IN LOVE BACK THEN?

READY? ACTION!

OKAY, SCENE 134. LET'S REHEARSE THE CAMERAWORK.

...

I CAN'T BELIEVE RICHIE MOORE, SKIRT-CHASING JUVENILE DELINQUENT, IS NOW A WORLD-FAMOUS DETECTIVE!

HA HA HA

YOU GAVE THE CLUE YOURSELF DURING THE INTRO, DUMMY.

HUH?

COME ON! YOU'RE NOT TELLING ME THAT'S YOUR ANSWER, ARE YOU?

...THE GRAY TABLECLOTH LOOKS WARMER THAN THE BLACK COAT!

...

SOME DETECTIVE YOUR FRIEND IS!

YOU DON'T THINK SO?

WHY DO YOU THINK *GRAY* LOOKS WARMER THAN *BLACK*, ANYWAY?

...OUT OF A—

THIS OLD MAN COULDN'T DETECT HIS WAY...

SHOW HIM WHAT YOU'VE GOT, RICHIE!

GET SERIOUS, DAD!

POK

SORRY. IT'S SUCH AN EASY CASE I THOUGHT I'D HAVE A LITTLE *FUN* WITH IT.

WHAT?

SLEEPING MOORE IN ACTION!!

LOOK!

OOG!

SHEESH.

THUP

TAKE A GOOD LOOK AT THE GOLF BAG PROPPED AGAINST THE FIRE-PLACE.

THE MURDERER THOUGHT THE POLICE WOULD SUSPECT HER IF SHE USED SOMETHING IN THE COLOR SHE LOVED.

TO PUT IT SIMPLY, THE MURDERER USED THE TABLECLOTH BECAUSE SHE WAS *AFRAID* TO USE THE COAT.

OUR CULPRIT IS THE WOMAN IN THE BLACK DRESS.

ALL THE FURNITURE AND CURTAINS IN THIS ROOM ARE BLACK, SUGGESTING THAT THE OWNER OF THE HOUSE IS FOND OF IT.

THE MURDERER PULLED IT OUT OF THE BAG TO USE AS THE MURDER WEAPON, THOUGHT TWICE ABOUT IT AND PULLED OUT A CLUB WITH A *WHITE* COVER INSTEAD.

NOTICE THE CLUB WITH THE BLACK COVER ON TOP OF THE OTHER CLUBS?

BLACK IS HER FAVORITE COLOR.

AAAAH!!

STOMP

RURI, THE WIDOW YOU'RE PLAYING IS THE KILLER!!

?

?

...AAM I RIGHT?

PERFECT DEDUC- TION!!

HUH? OH

OO O

WOW! YOU REALLY *ARE* THE FAMOUS SLEEPING MOORE!!

...

A REAL DETECTIVE SURE BEATS AN ACTOR!

WHY COULDN'T YOU GET IT RIGHT THE FIRST TIME?

UM... THANKS ...

YOU WERE GREAT, RICHIE!

I CAN GET THIS WHOLE SHOW *CANCELED* IF I WANT.

ANYONE ELSE WANNA STEP UP?

...

I'M GONNA GO TAKE A NAP. GO AHEAD AND SHOOT SOME SCENES AROUND ME.

HEH... WHAT A BORE.

EXACTLY. WHAT'S WORSE, THAT *BAD BOY ATTITUDE* HAS MADE HIM POPULAR WITH AUDIENCES. HE'S RATINGS GOLD.

I SEE. IS THAT WHERE HE GETS ALL HIS GOSSIP?

HE'S THE SON OF THE NEWSPAPER MOGUL WHO SPONSORS THIS SHOW!

WHO DOES HE THINK HE IS?

WHY DON'T WE TAKE A HALF-HOUR BREAK AND START FRESH?

AHH

A H E M !!

AT LEAST IT'S GIVEN ME AN EXCUSE TO SEE *YOU* AGAIN, RICHIE. ♡

...BUT MY AGENT TALKED ME INTO IT BECAUSE THIS SHOW IS SUCH A BIG HIT.

I DIDN'T WANT TO WORK ALONG-SIDE HIM...

THEY GOT IN A BIG FIGHT OVER SOY SAUCE VERSUS WORCESTERSHIRE SAUCE?

MOM AND DAD?

THEN, WHEN WE SAT DOWN TO SAMPLE THE FOOD, THEY STARTED EATING THE SAME DISHES IN EXACTLY THE SAME ORDER!

THE MYSTERY DEEPENS: HOW DID THOSE TWO EVER GET MARRIED?

EVA SAID FRIED EGGS WERE A WESTERN DISH, SO IT SHOULD BE WORCESTERSHIRE SAUCE! RICHIE SAID JAPANESE PEOPLE SHOULD ALWAYS USE SOY SAUCE!

SURE. IN HOME EC, THEY STARTED ARGUING OVER WHAT TO POUR OVER FRIED EGGS!

HUH...

THAT'S ENOUGH OLD STORIES...

I COULD NEVER TELL WHETHER YOU TWO WERE OPPOSITES... OR A *PERFECT MATCH.*

THEY SHOUTED AT EACH OTHER, "STOP COPYING ME!" THE WHOLE CLASS WAS LAUGHING!

WHAT IS IT?

MS. UJO?

HUH?

OH!

CHAK

NO, I WANT TO HEAR MORE!

HEY!

WE'VE ONLY GOT FIVE MINUTES OF BREAK TIME LEFT.

HEY! WHY DON'T WE GO OUTSIDE AND TAKE A LOOK?

THE FORECAST SAID IT MIGHT SNOW TODAY.

SNOW.

OKAY, OKAY!

IT'S THE FIRST SNOW OF THE YEAR!

JUST FOR FIVE MINUTES, THEN!

FRESH SNOW!

ISN'T IT GREAT?

I THOUGHT SHE CAME OUT WITH US.

HEY, WHERE'D RURI GO?

I DON'T SEE MISS RURI.

WHAT'S WRONG?

DON'T YOU LIKE IT, CONAN?

HE WAS ALREADY COVERED IN BLOOD WHEN I CAME IN HERE!!

NO! IT WASN'T ME!!

...

OF COURSE I BE-LIEVE YOU...

IT'S TRUE! YOU HAVE TO BELIEVE ME, RICHIE!!

WAAAH

NOW, NOW, KASU-MI...

IT'S NO USE CRYING! ANY ACTRESS CAN FAKE *THAT!*

...

I'M SURE WE CAN CLEAR THIS UP...

BUT WHAT IF THE POLICE SUSPECT YOU OR ME?

THE CAUSE OF DEATH IS LOSS OF BLOOD FROM A WOUND IN THE LEFT COMMON CAROTID ARTERY.

THE VICTIM IS YOSHIKI KAZAMI, AGE 28.

Shizuoka Police

...AND 8:20 P.M., WHEN THE BODY WAS DIS- COVERED.

THE ESTIMATED TIME OF DEATH IS SOMETIME BETWEEN 7:50 P.M., WHEN THE VICTIM ENTERED THIS ROOM TO TAKE A NAP...

HIS THROAT WAS SLASHED WITH A FOUR-INCH BLADE.

HE MUST HAVE BEEN ATTACKED WHILE NAPPING ON THIS SOFA.

...AND HEARD HIM SNOR- ING!

WHILE WE WERE LOOKING AROUND THE HOUSE, WE PASSED THIS ROOM...

HUH?

IT WAS PROBABLY CLOSER TO 8:20!

THAT MUST MEAN ...

RACHEL AND CONAN! WHAT'RE YOU DOING HERE?

YEAH. DAD CHECKED HIS WATCH AND COMMENTED THAT MR. KAZAMI HAD FALLEN ASLEEP IN JUST TEN MINUTES.

THAT WAS AROUND EIGHT O'CLOCK, RIGHT, RACHEL?

OF COURSE! AN EASY CASE TO CRACK!*

HA HA HA...

I HEAR YOU HELPED MY YOUNGER BROTHER THE OTHER DAY!

MR. MOORE!! YOU'RE HERE TOO!!

AHEM.

*Volume 34, File 9, "The Treacherous Towel"

NICE TO MEET YOU! I'M YOKO-MIZO FROM THE SHIZUOKA POLICE!!

YEAH!

RICHIE, YOU KNOW THIS MAN?

...AND MAYBE SHE IS...

WELL, MAYBE SHE ISN'T...

ER, WELL...

YOU'RE NOT HIS WIFE?

WHAT?

IT'S A PLEASURE TO FINALLY MEET YOU, MRS. MOORE!

HEY, I KNOW YOU!

I WAS JUST KIDDING.

SHE'S NOT!!

...AND YOU TOO!

...AND YOU...

AND I KNOW YOU...

ER, YES.

AREN'T YOU RURI UJO, THE ACTRESS?

THAT'S EXACTLY WHAT IT IS!

IT'S LIKE THE SET OF A *PRIME-TIME DRAMA!*

WHAT ARE ALL THESE TV STARS DOING HERE?

YOU RENTED THIS HOUSE DEEP IN THE FUJI COUNTRYSIDE TO SHOOT A MYSTERY DRAMA, AND THEN A REAL MURDER OCCURRED.

OKAY, LET ME GET THIS STRAIGHT.

THE ONLY PEOPLE WITHOUT ALIBIS ARE RURI UJO, WHO FOUND THE BODY...

DURING THE PERIOD FROM EIGHT O'CLOCK TO 8:20, EVERYONE WAS ON BREAK. THEY WERE MOSTLY IN GROUPS OF THREE OR MORE PEOPLE, SO ALMOST EVERYONE HAS AN ALIBI.

I GUESS SO...

AS THE SAYING GOES, "THE BITER WAS BIT."

YOU FOUR ARE OUR SUSPECTS!

...AND AKIRA'S SON, NOBUHARU NAGUMO.

...AKIRA NAGUMO...

THOSE WOULD BE KASUMI NAMIHARA...

...AND THREE PEOPLE WHO CLAIM THEY WERE ALONE IN THEIR ROOMS, REVIEWING THE SCRIPT.

I THOUGHT IT MIGHT CHEER HIM UP OUT OF HIS DARK MOOD.

I WENT TO MR. KAZAMI'S ROOM TO INVITE HIM TO ADMIRE THE SNOW WITH US.

I NOTICED IT HAD STARTED TO SNOW OUTSIDE, SO I URGED EVERYONE TO GO OUT AND ENJOY IT.

VERY WELL. I WAS LOOKING AROUND THE HOUSE WITH RICHIE... I MEAN, MR. MOORE... DURING THE BREAK.

MISS UJO, I'D LIKE YOU TO DESCRIBE EXACTLY HOW YOU FOUND THE BODY.

THAT'S WHEN I STARTED SCREAMING.

AT FIRST I THOUGHT HE WAS PULLING A PRANK. BUT WHEN I SHOOK HIM, HE DIDN'T RESPOND.

BUT WHEN I OPENED THE DOOR, HE WAS LYING ON THE FLOOR COVERED IN BLOOD.

WHY?

WHAT?

THEN LET'S START BY SENDING ALL FOUR OF YOU INTO ANOTHER ROOM TO BE SEARCHED.

THAT'S RIGHT!

YES.

AND THE THREE OF YOU CAME RUNNING WHEN YOU HEARD HER SCREAM, RIGHT?

...BUT THE FOUR-INCH BLADE THAT SLICED KAZAMI'S THROAT IS NOWHERE TO BE FOUND.

WE'VE COMBED THE ENTIRE BUILDING...

DID YOU FIND THE WEAPON?

INSPECTOR YOKOMIZO!!

TIK TIK TIK

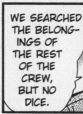

WE SEARCHED THE BELONGINGS OF THE REST OF THE CREW, BUT NO DICE.

NONE OF THE FOUR WAS CARRYING ANY KIND OF BLADE.

WE'RE SEARCHING THE DRAINS AND GOING OVER THE GROUNDS WITH METAL DETECTORS, BUT NOTHING'S COME UP SO FAR.

AND ALL WE FOUND ON THE VICTIM'S PERSON WERE CIGARETTES, A LIGHTER AND A WALLET.

WE DIDN'T GET A LUMINOL REACTION FROM ANY OF THEM.

IN THE ENTIRE HOUSE, THE ONLY POSSIBLE WEAPONS WE FOUND WERE A BREAD KNIFE AND FRUIT KNIFE, BOTH IN THE KITCHEN, AND A UTILITY KNIFE WITH A SHORT BLADE FOUND IN A CREWMAN'S TOOLBOX.

ANYONE COULD'VE TAKEN THEM.

THE GLOVES AND COAT ARE PROPS FROM THE SHOW. THE ROOM WHERE THEY WERE KEPT WAS EMPTY DURING THE BREAK.

...SO WHY CAN'T WE FIND THE WEAPON?

WE FOUND THE COAT AND GOLF GLOVES THE MURDERER PROBABLY WORE TO COMMIT THE CRIME...

WAITING UPSTAIRS WITH MR. MOORE.

WHERE ARE THE FOUR SUSPECTS NOW?

DARN IT!

CHK CHK

ARGH!

I'M THE SAME WAY!

I GREW UP TO DISLIKE SMOKING TOO.

OH YEAH! HE WAS FAMOUS IN THE NEIGHBORHOOD AS A BIG ANTI-SMOKER!

HAVE YOU FORGOTTEN WHAT MY DAD WAS LIKE?

SURE. DON'T YOU?

YOU SMOKE, RICHIE?

WE HAVE TO BEG THE DIRECTOR NOT TO MAKE US SMOKE!

USUALLY I JUST PUT A CIGARETTE IN MY MOUTH AND PRETEND.

AREN'T THERE SCENES WHERE YOU HAVE TO SMOKE IN TV DRAMAS?

DAD USED TO BE A HEAVY SMOKER, BUT SHE CONVINCED HIM TO QUIT ONCE I WAS BORN.

MY MOM ALWAYS HATED CIGA- RETTES.

KASU- MI...

IF YOU HAD MORE DEDICATION TO YOUR CRAFT, MAYBE YOU'D BE KNOWN AS MORE THAN JUST AN ACTOR'S SON!

SHE'S JUST JEAL- OUS.

WHAT WAS THAT ALL ABOUT?

HMPH...

...GETS SOME MILEAGE OUT OF PROMOT- ING HER SQUEAKY- CLEAN IMAGE.

KOFF

BUT I GUESS "JAPAN'S SWEET- HEART" HERE...

THOSE TWO ARE AN ITEM.

LOOKS LIKE KAZAMI WAS RIGHT.

CUTE, ISN'T IT?

I GOT A LITTLE TOO CLOSE TO *HIM*.

HEH

... WELL ...

IF HE WAS ALSO RIGHT ABOUT *THIS GUY* HAVING A YOUNGER GIRLFRIEND...

...IT COULD BE...

EXCUSE ME, MR. MOORE.

UM... NOT YET...

SO HAVE YOU IDENTIFIED THE MURDERER, MR. GREAT DETECTIVE?

...

OKAY, WHAT'S UP?

THE BATH-ROOM!

CONAN, WHERE ARE YOU GOING?

TAKKA

UH, SURE.

MAY WE SPEAK?

...

HUH?

JUST WHAT DO YOU THINK YOU'RE DOING?

YES, SIR!

HMMM?

IS THAT REALLY ALL THERE IS TO IT?

I DON'T HAVE ANY INTENTIONS! WE'RE JUST *CHILDHOOD* FRIENDS!

HUH? YOU MEAN RURI?

WHAT ARE YOUR INTENTIONS TOWARD HER?

I'VE BEEN THROUGH THIS BEFORE.

WAIT A SEC.

SEE THAT YOU WATCH YOURSELF. NO MATTER HOW MUCH OF A *CELEBRITY* YOU MAY BE, I WON'T PUT UP WITH ANY FUNNY BUSINESS.

VERY WELL, THEN.

THE TIME I...

IT'S LIKE THE TIME...

THIS TOOLBOX WAS LEFT IN THE SAME ROOM AS THE COAT AND GLOVES, RIGHT?

HEY, KID! WHAT'RE YOU DOING?

CHUK

CHUK

HEY! WHAT IDIOT PUT A BLOCKING MARK HERE?

YEAH!

EVEN THIS TAPE MEASURE?

I DON'T MIND LITTLE BOYS PLAYING DETECTIVE, BUT THE COPS ALREADY SEARCHED THAT TOOLBOX.

I THOUGHT IT MIGHT CONTAIN SOMETHING SHARP BESIDES THAT UTILITY KNIFE.

WAIT!!

...BUT I'LL PEEL IT OFF JUST IN CASE—

I'M SURE THEY'RE GOING TO CALL OFF THE SHOOT...

IT SHOWS WHERE TO PLACE THE PROPS AND MAKE THE ACTORS STAND!

IT'S A MARK MADE ON THE FLOOR WITH GAFFER TAPE!

WHAT'S A BLOCKING MARK?

AND THERE'S SOMETHING STUCK TO ONE EDGE...

IT BULGES IN THE MIDDLE.

THERE'S SOMETHING FUNNY ABOUT THIS TAPE.

?!

COTTON?

WHAT IS THIS?

SNIFF SNIFF

...AND WHY THE POLICE CAN'T FIND IT!!

I KNOW WHAT THE WEAPON WAS...

THE ONLY QUESTION IS *WHO DID IT.*

WITH THE ROOMS SO CLOSE TOGETHER, IT WAS NO PROBLEM FOR THE MURDERER TO GET IN AND OUT.

THE SCENE OF THE CRIME IS ACROSS THE HALL.

HERE'S THE ROOM WHERE THE COAT AND GLOVES WERE KEPT.

RURI WAS WEIRDLY INSISTENT ABOUT MAKING ALL OF US GO OUTSIDE TO LOOK AT THE SNOW. WHY?

SOME-THING'S BEEN BUGGING ME.

HEY!!

SHK

HE'S PLAYING AROUND THE CRIME SCENE AGAIN!

THAT BRAT!

IT'S MR. MOORE!!

OH SHOOT!

THAT'S WHY!!

I SEE!!

WHERE'D THAT RASCAL GO?

HE LEFT THE ROOM A LITTLE WHILE AGO.

WHERE'S INSPECTOR YOKO-MIZO?

...HERE'S THE WALLET...

ER... HERE'S THE COAT, HERE ARE THE GLOVES...

OF COURSE.

AH! I, UM, NEED TO CHECK THE EVIDENCE AGAIN. COULD I BORROW A PAIR OF GLOVES?

NOPE.

YOU GUYS DON'T HAPPEN TO SMOKE, DO YOU?

I JUST NEED TO PUT MR. MOORE TO SLEEP AND—

OKAY, I'VE CRACKED THIS CASE.

...AND HERE...

CHK

I USED MY LAST DART DURING THE REHEARSAL!!

I FORGOT!!

WHERE'S THE TRANQUILIZER DART?

POK

UH-OH!

HUH?

POK

I CAN'T DO THE SLEEPING MOORE ROUTINE!

SHEESH! WHAT NOW?

...

FILE 4:
RICHARD'S CHOICE ③

...I CAN'T TURN MR. MOORE INTO SLEEPING MOORE!!

IF I CAN'T USE THE TRANQ DART...

POK

I'LL DROP HINTS UNTIL MR. MOORE CRACKS THE CASE HIMSELF.

I'LL JUST HAVE TO WING IT.

I DON'T NEED ANY MORE HELP.

HMPH.

WHAT?

HUH?

UM... HI, MR. MOORE!

I'VE NOTICED SOME FUNNY STUFF! WANNA HEAR ABOUT IT?

MAYBE IT COULD HELP YOU SOLVE THE CASE!

...HE'S SOLVED IT ON HIS OWN?

DOES THIS MEAN...

HAVE YOU FOUND A DEADLY WEAPON?

YEAH?

OH, JUST LOOKING AROUND THE HOUSE, SEARCHING FOR THE KEY TO SOLVE THIS CASE.

MR. MOORE!! I'VE BEEN LOOKING ALL OVER FOR YOU!!

WHERE HAVE YOU BEEN?

HE HASN'T SOLVED ANY-THING.

NAH, JUST THIS DEAD WEIGHT.

HUH?

SLAM

SURE, NO PROB!

ARRGH... IF ONLY I COULD KNOCK HIM OUT...

I SEE. WELL, THE SEARCH IS STILL ON. LET ME KNOW IF YOU FIND ANYTHING.

HE'S CRACKED THE CASE!

IT'S TRUE!

HE LOOKS SO SERIOUS!

HEY!

WHAT?

...I NEED TO TALK TO YOU.

RURI...

MAYBE I CAN KICK SOMETHING INTO HIS HEAD AND KNOCK HIM OUT.

KLIK

WHAT NOW?

DON'T GO OFF WITH HER!!

NO!!

SLAM

THE DOOR!

HEY!

CHK

BEEET

SOME-THING...

CHAK

SOME-THING HEAVY.

I'VE GOT TO GET INSIDE!

IT'S LOCKED!

...

ARE YOU TRYING TO SEDUCE ME?

WHY'D YOU LOCK THE DOOR?

WHAT'S THE MATTER, RICHIE?

...WILL FIT UNDER THE DOOR...

PIK

HOPE-FULLY THIS WIRE-TAP...

POK

I CAN'T HEAR WHAT THEY'RE SAYING.

TOK

TOK

IS THAT IT?

BUT I'M NOT TALKING ABOUT YOU.

NO! SHE'S NOT THE KILLER!

I'VE GOT TO STOP HIM!

I WANT TO CATCH THAT KILLER.

YEAH, THAT'S RIGHT.

OR DO YOU THINK I'M THE ONE WHO KILLED KAZAMI? IS THIS ALL ABOUT CATCHING THE KILLER?

I'M TALKING ABOUT *AKIRA NAGUMO*, THE GUY YOU'RE COVERING FOR!!

YOU SAW IT, DIDN'T YOU? JUST BEFORE YOU SAW THE SNOW OUTSIDE.

WHY WOULD I TRY TO COVER FOR MR. NAGUMO?

WHAT ARE YOU TALKING ABOUT, RICHIE?

WHAT?

THAT DOOR HAD A *MIRROR* ON IT.

A CREWMAN OPENED THE DOOR TO THE ROOM NEAR THE WINDOW.

S... SAW WHAT?

HE DUCKED BACK INTO THE ROOM BEFORE ANYONE ELSE COULD SPOT HIM, BUT YOU'D SEEN HIM CLEARLY!

IN THE REFLECTION, YOU SAW NAGUMO ABOUT TO STEP OUT OF THE ROOM WHERE KAZAMI HAD BEEN SLEEPING.

HIS REFLECTION IN THE MIRROR ON THE DOOR WAS CLEAR AS DAY.

I REALIZED IT JUST A MOMENT AGO. AS I CAME AROUND THE CORNER, I SAW CONAN STANDING IN FRONT OF THE ROOM WHERE THE MURDER TOOK PLACE.

IF HE COULDN'T GET OUT OF THAT ROOM BEFORE THE BREAK ENDED, IT'D BE ALL OVER FOR HIM.

REALIZING HE MUST HAVE DONE SOMETHING WRONG, YOU PERSUADED EVERYBODY TO GO OUTSIDE AND LOOK AT THE SNOW, GIVING HIM TIME TO ESCAPE.

I'D LIKE TO CONGRATU-LATE YOU ON YOUR DEDUCTION, MR. SLEUTH...

AFTER YOU GOT EVERY-BODY OUTSIDE, YOU WENT TO THE SCENE OF THE CRIME, FOUND KAZAMI'S BODY AND SCREAMED!

WHERE'S THE BLADE MR. NAGUMO SUPPOSEDLY USED TO SLIT KAZAMI'S THROAT?

...BUT IF THAT'S TRUE, WHERE'S THE WEAPON?

WHAT?

...THEY NEVER THOUGHT IT MIGHT HAVE BEEN BROKEN INTO *LITTLE PIECES*.

RIGHT, THE FOUR-INCH BLADE. EVERY-ONE'S BEEN SO HUNG UP ON THE LENGTH...

SHOULDN'T YOU BE LOOKING FOR THE MISSING FOUR-INCH BLADE RATHER THAN MAKING UP SOME CRAZY STORY CASTING ME AS AN ACCOMPLICE TO MURDER?

AFTER SLITTING KAZAMI'S THROAT, THE MURDERER SNAPPED THE BLADE INTO TINY PIECES AND HID THEM...

THE UTILITY KNIFE.

I CAN'T BELIEVE HE GOT IT RIGHT!

WOW!

...KAZAMI WAS CARRYING!

...INSIDE THE LIGHTER...

...EVEN IF THERE *IS* A BLADE HIDDEN IN THAT LIGHTER, IT CAN'T BE THE WEAPON.

BUT, RICHIE...

TELL HER!

THIS IS IT, MR. MOORE.

YOU CAN'T CUT SOMEBODY THAT DEEPLY WITHOUT A BLADE FASTENED TO A HILT. AND BLOOD WOULD SPLATTER ALL OVER IT.

THE KNIFE WENT *FOUR INCHES* INTO KAZAMI'S THROAT.

THE POLICE DIDN'T GET A LUMINOL REACTION FROM THE UTILITY KNIFE. SO WHERE'S THE HILT OF THE WEAPON?

HEY, CONAN! WHAT'RE YOU DOING HERE?

FOR THE LOVE OF—

TAK

SEE?

I... DON'T KNOW.

RACHEL...

R...

UM, ER...

WITHOUT THE HILT OF THE KNIFE, YOU HAVEN'T GOT A CASE.

"...TAPE?"

HUH?

...CAN I HAVE SOME BUBBLE-GUM...

TAPE!!

THAT'S IT!!

I'VE GOT SOME STICKS OF GUM, BUT I DON'T THINK I HAVE IT IN *TAPE* FORM...

...

TAPE?

EH?

...WENT INTO THE ROOM WHERE KAZAMI WAS SLEEPING, KILLED HIM, SNAPPED THE BLADES OFF AND HID THEM IN THE LIGHTER.

NAGUMO TOOK THE COAT, GLOVES, KNIFE AND GAFFER TAPE FROM THE SET IN THE ROOM ACROSS THE HALL...

THE MURDERER KEPT BLOOD FROM GETTING ON THE HILT OF THE KNIFE BY WRAPPING IT IN GAFFER TAPE!

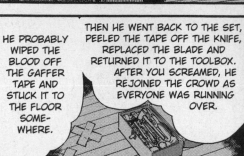

HE PROBABLY WIPED THE BLOOD OFF THE GAFFER TAPE AND STUCK IT TO THE FLOOR SOME-WHERE.

THEN HE WENT BACK TO THE SET, PEELED THE TAPE OFF THE KNIFE, REPLACED THE BLADE AND RETURNED IT TO THE TOOLBOX. AFTER YOU SCREAMED, HE REJOINED THE CROWD AS EVERYONE WAS RUNNING OVER.

YOU? YOU WOULDN'T HURT A FLY!

MAYBE I MADE EVERY-ONE GO OUTSIDE SO I COULD SNEAK BACK IN AND KILL HIM MYSELF!

I COULD'VE DONE THE SAME THING, AND I WAS THE ONE WHO FOUND THE BODY!!

BUT WHAT MAKES YOU THINK MR. NAGUMO DID IT?

THAT FLOOR WAS COVERED IN TAPE FOR BLOCKING, SO NO ONE WOULD NOTICE IT.

WHAT?

CAN YOU SHOW ME HOW TO TAKE OFF A BRA?

YES?

ER, RACHEL?

SORRY, CONAN. I THINK I LEFT MY GUM IN THE RENTAL CAR.

SHE'S ONE TOUGH LADY...

I'VE NEVER USED ONE BEFORE!! HOW WOULD I KNOW HOW TO TAKE IT APART?

?

SORRY, RACHEL...

YOU NAUGHTY BOY!! YOU DON'T NEED TO KNOW *THAT*!!

!!

ER... INSIDE THE LID, OF COURSE.

TELL ME, WHERE IN THIS LIGHTER WOULD YOU HIDE THE BLADES?

WHY NOT?

RURI, YOU COULDN'T HAVE COMMITTED THIS CRIME.

THE MURDERER REMOVED THE OUTER COVER AND TOOK OUT THE COTTON STUFFING...

POP

THIS TYPE OF LIGHTER HAS A CARTRIDGE STUFFED WITH COTTON. IT FIRES BY DOUSING THE COTTON WITH LIGHTER FLUID.

WHAT?

POK

YOU'VE NEVER USED A CIGARETTE LIGHTER IN YOUR LIFE. YOU COULDN'T HAVE THOUGHT OF THIS PLAN.

I NOTICED THE COTTON HAD BEEN TAKEN OUT OF THIS LIGHTER WHEN I TRIED TO USE IT TO LIGHT UP.

...

CHK CHK

...TO HIDE THE PIECES OF THE BLADE INSIDE.

KLK

KLK

...AND HE'S THE ONE PERSON YOU'D WANT TO PROTECT.

BUT AKIRA NAGUMO USED TO BE A HEAVY SMOKER...

...BUT IT'S NOT LIKE WE'RE CLOSE.

SURE, I KNOW HIM THROUGH MY WORK...

WHY WOULD I WANT TO COVER FOR MR. NAGUMO?

HAVEN'T WE BEEN OVER THIS?

?

...YOUR LOVER.

...BE-CAUSE HE'S...

YOU **ARE** CLOSE...

...YOUR FATHER.

NOTHING USED IN THE CRIME WAS PREPARED IN ADVANCE.

I BET NAGUMO DECIDED TO KILL KAZAMI ON THE SPUR OF THE MOMENT.

...

HE'S *WHAT?*

HUH?

AND HE HAD TO RIG THE KNIFE AND THE LIGHTER QUICKLY, WHICH MEANS HE PROBABLY WASN'T WEARING GLOVES.

IT SHOULD BE EASY TO FIND THE BITS OF COTTON. THEY'RE PROBABLY HIDDEN UNDER THE TAPE ON THE FLOOR.

SHF

...I WANT YOU TO PERSUADE YOUR FATHER—

BEFORE ANY OF THAT EVIDENCE COMES TO LIGHT...

NOT BAD, MR. MOORE.

YOU OUTDID ME.

WE'LL FIND HIS FINGERPRINTS ALL OVER THEM.

SHE ONLY REALIZED THAT SHE WAS PREGNANT AFTER SHE'D LEFT THEIR THEATER GROUP AND MET THE MAN SHE EVENTUALLY MARRIED, THE MAN I ALWAYS KNEW AS MY FATHER.

MY MOTHER DATED NAGUMO WHILE THEY WERE BOTH STRUGGLING YOUNG ACTORS.

AKIRA NAGUMO IS MY BIOLOGICAL FATHER.

THAT'S RIGHT, RICHIE.

...UNTIL I APPEARED WITH NAGUMO IN A TV DRAMA. HE KEPT TELLING ME I WAS THE SPITTING IMAGE OF MY MOTHER.

I NEVER SUS-PECTED IT...

AFTER ALL, HE'S STILL MY FATHER.

I AGREED TO MEET WITH HIM IN SECRET.

BUT HE STARTED TO CRY RIGHT IN FRONT OF ME.

I TOLD HIM IT WAS TOO LATE FOR HIM TO BE MY FATHER!

I FORCED MY MOTHER TO TELL ME THE TRUTH. NAGUMO STARTED CALLING ME, ASKING TO SEE ME.

...PLEASE, RICHIE...

SO...

IF THE TRUTH CAME OUT, IT WOULD TEAR MY FAMILY APART.

HE KILLED KAZAMI FOR MY SAKE.

IT WAS A FATHER WORRIED ABOUT HIS LITTLE GIRL. I WENT THROUGH THE SAME THING WHEN I TOLD EVA'S DAD WE WERE AN ITEM.

IT WASN'T THE ATTITUDE OF A MAN JEALOUS OVER ANOTHER GUY PUTTING THE MOVES ON HIS GIRLFRIEND.

IT WAS HIS *ATTITUDE* THAT GAVE IT AWAY.

...WHY I STUDIED SO HARD AS A KID THAT I ENDED UP NEEDING GLASSES?

DO YOU KNOW...

JUST HER BLOWHARD OF A DAD!

NO, I WASN'T THINK-ING ABOUT EVA!

I CAN NEVER BEAT HER, CAN I?

SIGH... EVA AGAIN.

...OF A BOY WHO HAD A THING FOR *BRAINY GIRLS.*

I WANTED TO GET THE ATTEN-TION...

...AND THE MYSTERY DRAMA CAME TO A CLOSE.

THIRTY MINUTES LATER, RURI CONVINCED NAGUMO TO TURN HIMSELF IN...

HUH?

...THE GRAY TABLE-CLOTH LOOKS WARMER THAN THE BLACK COAT!

DOESN'T IT MAKE YOU THINK OF A WARM, FURRY ANIMAL?

IT'S MOUSE-COLORED!

NO, NOTHING!

WHAT? DID I SAY SOMETHING FUNNY?

YOU'RE SUCH A STRANGE GIRL.

WHAT IS IT?

HE'S SUCH A STRANGE GUY.

ZZZZZ

ZZZZZ

RICHARD MOORE P.I.

HIS MOTIVE IS NONE OF MY BUSINESS.

IS THAT TRUE?

WHEN MR. NAGUMO WAS ARRESTED, HE SAID HE KILLED MR. KAZAMI BECAUSE HE COULDN'T TAKE SEEING KAZAMI ATTACK HIS SON.

WHAT CAN YOU TELL US ABOUT THE MURDER?

EXCUSE ME! DETECTIVE MOORE!!

...AND ADVISE HIM TO TURN HIMSELF IN WHILE HE HAD THE CHANCE.

ALL I DID WAS LOCATE THE MISSING WEAPON ...

TURNING MY BACK TO THE PRESS...

MR. MOORE!!

WAIT! MR. MOORE!

THAT'S ALL!

NOW THAT HE'S ACTUALLY SOLVED A CASE HIMSELF, THERE'S NO TEARING HIM AWAY FROM THE TV.

SHEESH... USUALLY HE HAS TO WATCH HIS CASES ON THE NEWS JUST TO FIND OUT WHAT HE DID.

I LOOK SOOOO COOL!

...MASAMI HIROTA, THE WOMAN SHOT TO DEATH IN THE TEN-BILLION-YEN ROBBERY CASE...

GIN AND VODKA, THE TWO GUYS WHO GAVE ME THE DRUG THAT TURNED ME INTO A KID...

I'VE MET SEVEN PEOPLE WHO WERE DEFINITELY MEMBERS OF THE SYNDICATE.

I'M TRYING TO MAKE MR. MOORE FAMOUS TO GET THE ATTENTION OF THE MEN IN BLACK AND LEARN MORE ABOUT THEM, BUT SO FAR THE PLAN'S BEEN A BUST.

LET'S WATCH THAT TAPE ONE MORE TIME!

...KIICHIRO NUMABUCHI, WHO ESCAPED FROM THE SYNDICATE'S SECRET LABORATORIES AND WAS ARRESTED BY THE POLICE...

...PISCO, WHO WAS KILLED BY GIN AT A FILM FESTIVAL...

...TEQUILA, WHO DIED IN AN EXPLOSION AT THE UNVEILING OF A NEW COMPUTER GAME...

MASAMI HIROTA'S REAL NAME WAS AKEMI MIYANO, AND PISCO CALLED ANITA "SHIHO," SO ANITA'S REAL NAME IS PROBABLY SHIHO MIYANO.

...AND ANITA HAILEY, CODE NAME SHERRY. SHE'S MASAMI HIROTA'S YOUNGER SISTER AND THE CREATOR OF THE DRUG THAT SHRANK US.

A VIDEO GAME?

WHAT?

DETECTIVE MOORE'S OFFICE...

I DOUBT THEY'RE PLANNING TO SPEND ALL THAT MONEY TO RELEASE A COOL NEW VIDEO GAME.

THE MEN IN BLACK HAVE ACQUIRED HUGE AMOUNTS OF MONEY THROUGH HIGH-LEVEL ASSASSINATIONS, THEY'VE DEVELOPED STRANGE NEW DRUGS AND THEY SEEM INTERESTED IN RECRUITING SKILLED COMPUTER PROGRAMMERS. BUT WHY?

BRRRNG

I'VE GOTTA RETAPE TODAY'S RERUN OF YOKO OKINO'S TV DRAMA SO I CAN CUT OUT THE COMMERCIALS!

TELL 'EM I'M OUT!

...

A SOFTWARE ENGINEER WORKING FOR YOUR VIDEO GAME COMPANY IS MISSING?

WHAT?

YES... YES... AND YOU WANT US TO FIND HIM...

HEY!

MY DAD SEEMS TO BE FREE!

SURE, COME DOWN TO THE OFFICE RIGHT AWAY!

A SOFTWARE ENGINEER, KIDNAPPED?

OKAY, OKAY!

STRAIGHTEN YOUR TIE AND SHAVE!

KLIK

...THE MEN IN BLACK?

COULD IT BE...

THAT'S RIGHT. HE OFTEN DISAPPEARS WHEN WE'RE CLOSE TO A BIG DEADLINE.

...THIS ISN'T THE FIRST TIME YOU'VE LOST HIM.

YOU SAID...

SO THIS IS MR. ITAKURA, THE PROGRAMMER WHO WENT MISSING A WEEK AGO.

HMM...

WELL, WE CAN'T SIT AROUND WAITING FOR HIM TO RESURFACE ANY LONGER.

I THINK HE'S JUST AVOIDING OUR CALLS.

HE SAYS HE ISOLATES HIMSELF SO NO ONE CAN BREAK HIS CONCENTRATION.

HANG ON! WE'RE PAYING FOR THE SLEUTH TOO!

...PLEASE CALL US—

IF YOU MANAGE TO TRACK HIM DOWN...

SURE DOESN'T SOUND LIKE THE MEN IN BLACK AT WORK.

HMM...

THE LAST TIME THIS HAPPENED WE CALLED THE POLICE, AND HE THREW A FIT OVER IT. WE THOUGHT YOU COULD BE MORE DISCREET.

DON'T YOU ALL WORK FOR THE SAME COMPANY?

OUR COMPANY WAS THE FIRST TO CALL THIS GUY'S AGENCY! WE SHOULD GET THE INFO FIRST!

MY NAME'S SOMA.

WE HIRED HIM TO CREATE A SHOGI GAME.

HE'S DEVELOPING A CHESS GAME FOR US.

I'M NAITO.

MY NAME'S SUGAI.

MY COMPANY ASKED ITAKURA TO CREATE A VIRTUAL GO GAME.

RYUSUKE SOMA (44) GAME COMPANY EXECUTIVE

JOHEI NAITO (47) GAME COMPANY EXECUTIVE

KATSUMICHI SUGAI (39) GAME COMPANY EXECUTIVE

WE ALL BELIEVED THAT SLICK OPERATOR!

WHEN WE HIRED HIM, HE TOLD EACH OF US HE WASN'T WORKING ON ANY OTHER PROJECTS.

THAT'S WHY WE WANT TO FIND HIM! TO CONFRONT HIM ABOUT LYING TO US!

THREE COMPUTERIZED BOARD GAMES AT ONCE? CAN ONE PROGRAMMER DO ALL THAT?

LAST WEEK EACH OF US RECEIVED AN EMAIL WITH A PHOTO OF ITAKURA AND A RECORDING OF HIS VOICE.

HOW'D YOU FIND OUT HE WAS TRYING TO DO THREE JOBS AT ONCE?

I THINK I'LL WORK AWAY FROM MY OFFICE FOR A WHILE. KEEP YOUR HATS ON, OKAY?

BUT LATELY MY HEART'S BEEN PRETTY STRONG.

IT HASN'T BEEN EASY DOING THREE JOBS AT ONCE.

WE CALLED SOME LOCAL HOTELS, BUT THEY WERE ALL VERY PROTECTIVE OF THEIR GUESTS' PRIVACY.

IT LOOKS LIKE IT WAS TAKEN IN A HOTEL ROOM.

NOW HOW CAN I FIND ITAKURA WITH JUST A *PHOTO* TO GO ON?

I KNOW THE GUY YOU'RE TALKING ABOUT. HE DIED IN AN EXPLOSION, SO HE COULDN'T BE INVOLVED IN THIS.

HUH? THAT'S JAPANESE, CHINESE *AND* WESTERN FOOD!

HEY, RACHEL! CAN WE HAVE SUSHI, EGG FOO YONG AND BEEF STEW FOR LUNCH TODAY?

...

HE PROBABLY CHECKED IN UNDER A FALSE NAME ANYWAY...

WAIT A SEC!

IF I ORDERED ALL THAT STUFF AT ONCE, THE WAITERS WOULD THINK I WAS PRETTY WEIRD, HUH?

NOT EVEN A BIG FAMILY RESTAURANT WILL HAVE ALL THAT!

AND HE DIDN'T TAKE ANYTHING ELSE?

ONE OF HIS EMPLOYEES TOLD ME HE TOOK HIS LAPTOP AND A FEW COMPUTER DISKS.

DO YOU KNOW IF HE TOOK ANYTHING OUT OF HIS OFFICE WHEN HE LEFT?

...THIS GUY'S GOT A SHOGI BOARD, A GO BOARD AND A CHESSBOARD IN HIS ROOM!

COME TO THINK OF IT...

THE PHONE IN MY ROOM ISN'T WORKING!! I'M CALLING FROM MY CELL PHONE, AND I EXPECT YOU TO FIX THIS PROBLEM IMMEDIATELY!!

I'M THE GUEST WHO BORROWED A SET OF SHOGI, CHESS AND GO BOARDS!!

I'M SORRY. WHO IS THIS?

WHAT IS WRONG WITH THIS HOTEL?

OKAY, NEXT UP...

KLIK

OOPS, SORRY, WRONG NUMBER!

WE HAVEN'T LOANED OUT ANY BOARD GAMES TO GUESTS TODAY...

...WOULD BE THE TALK OF THE HOTEL STAFF!

A STRANGE GUEST LIKE THAT...

NO ONE ELSE WOULD ORDER A BUNCH OF BOARD GAMES FROM THE FRONT DESK AND HANG ON TO THEM FOR A WEEK.

CHING

...THE NEW BAKER HOTEL!

AH, YES. MR. ITAKURA IN ROOM 2004, RIGHT?

I'M CALLING FROM MY CELL PHONE, AND I EXPECT YOU TO FIX THIS PROBLEM—

IT LOOKS LIKE THE PHONE WAS JUST UNPLUGGED!

OH, WAIT!

NEVER MIND!!

KLIK

I'LL SEND SOMEONE UP TO YOUR ROOM RIGHT AWAY.

ITAKURA IN ROOM 2004, THAT'S ME!

ER... RIGHT...

...ROOM 2004!!

NEW BAKER HOTEL...

IT'S NOT FAIR, MR. MOORE! AFTER YOU GET PAID FOR SOLVING THE CASE, YOU'RE GONNA HAVE A FANCY MEAL AT THE HOTEL RESTAURANT, RIGHT?

BUT CONAN WANTED TO COME!

YOU'LL JUST GET IN THE WAY!!

AND *WHY* ARE YOU TWO COMING ALONG?

ONCE WE FIND ITAKURA, WE'LL TREAT YOU *ALL* TO DINNER!

DON'T WORRY ABOUT IT, SIR!

HMPH

VROOOM

WHY'D YOU COME TO ME AS A GROUP?

SHF

ONE THING'S BEEN BUGGING ME. AREN'T YOU ALL *BUSINESS RIVALS?*

SO THIS IS HIS HIDEOUT, HUH?

SKREE

THAT'S WHEN I CAME UP WITH THE IDEA OF HIRING *YOU*, MR. MOORE.

SINCE WE WERE LOOKING FOR HIM TOO, WE DECIDED TO MEET EACH OTHER AND DISCUSS THE PROBLEM.

ONCE I FOUND OUT ITAKURA WAS WORKING THREE JOBS AT ONCE, I STARTED CALLING OTHER GAME COMPANIES!

I SHOULD'VE JUST MADE THEM PAY ME AT THE OFFICE. THEY COULD'VE GONE TO THE HOTEL THEM-SELVES.

SIGH... I'M MISSING YOKO'S TV SHOW.

SHEESH.

STEP OFF, BOTH OF YOU! *I'M* THE ONE WHO CALLED HIS OFFICE!

BUT I'M THE ONE WHO SUG-GESTED MR. MOORE!

HEY, IT WAS *ME!* I SAID WE SHOULD HIRE A DETEC-TIVE!

I THINK YOURS IS A KNOCK-OFF!

COME ON, IT'S BRAND-NEW! I JUST BOUGHT IT FIVE DAYS AGO!

NO WAY IS THAT REAL!

ME TOO!

I CAME PRE-PARED!

HE'S VERY PICKY ABOUT WATCHES.

WHAT?

OH, ITAKURA'S NOT GOING TO LIKE THAT CHEAP WATCH OF YOURS!

SIGH...

SURE.

MR. NAITO, WOULD YOU PRESS THE BUTTON FOR THE 20TH FLOOR?

UM... RIGHT...

ITAKURA'S GOING TO BE SO SURPRISED WHEN HE SEES ALL OF US!

PIP

VNNN

IF ITAKURA KNOWS THE MEN IN BLACK...

MAYBE THIS ISN'T SUCH A GOOD IDEA.

BDMP

A HIT MAN COULD BE IN HIS ROOM RIGHT NOW!

MAYBE ITAKURA WAS ONE OF THE MEN IN BLACK HIMSELF, AND HE'S BEEN ON THE RUN FROM THEIR ASSASSINS!

DOES THAT MEAN THE SYNDICATE'S TRYING TO KILL HIM?

TEQUILA TOLD HIM, "I'VE GOT NO USE FOR YOU ANYMORE!"

BDMP

...BARGING INTO HIS ROOM!

...IT MIGHT NOT BE SAFE TO SEND RACHEL, MR. MOORE AND THESE GUYS...

BDMP

OR HE WOULD'VE TRIED TO HUSH HIM UP, AND IT DOESN'T LOOK LIKE *THAT* HAPPENED.

AND IF ITAKURA WERE ONE OF THE MEN IN BLACK, HE WOULDN'T HAVE LET SOMA INTO HIS OFFICE WHILE HE WAS TALKING WITH TEQUILA.

IF THE MEN IN BLACK HAD WANTED TO KILL ITAKURA, HE'D BE LONG DEAD BY NOW!

TEQUILA SAID THAT TWO YEARS AGO!

NAH, I'M GETTING PARANOID. CHILL OUT, JIMMY!

...THAT MEETING WITH TEQUILA.

CHING

ZHHK

ANYWAY, I'LL JUST HAVE TO MEET ITAKURA AND TRY TO GET HIM TO TALK ABOUT...

DING DONG

DING DONG

THE DOOR LOCKS AUTOMATICALLY, SO PLEASE REMEMBER TO CARRY YOUR ROOM KEY!

I'M SO SORRY ABOUT THIS!

WE CAN WAIT HERE.

HE MUST'VE GONE OUT FOR A BITE TO EAT.

HUH. I DON'T SEE A "DO NOT DISTURB" SIGN.

KLK

HURRY! I'VE GOTTA GO POTTY!

OKAY, OKAY!

HUH?

I GUESS HE FORGOT WE WERE COMING TO SEE HIM!

EXCUSE ME, MISTER! CAN YOU OPEN MY UNCLE'S ROOM TOO?

THIS WAY WE CAN SURPRISE HIM!

IF MR. ITAKURA SEES US OUT IN THE HALL, HE MIGHT TRY TO RUN AWAY.

SMART WORK, LITTLE BOY!

ER... THANKS A LOT.

HERE YOU GO!

CHAK

TAKKA

WHAT?

LOOKS LIKE WE WON'T NEED TO DO THAT.

THAT'S OKAY, KID.

YOU CAN'T ESCAPE US NOW, MR. ITAKU—

HEY, WAKE UP!

THE NERVE OF THAT GUY!

ITAKURA'S NAPPING AT HIS DESK.

A DIARY!!

Diary

IT COULD TELL ME WHY TEQUILA CAME TO SEE ITAKURA...

BUT IF THAT DISK CONTAINS HIS DAILY JOURNAL, IT COULD BE THE CLUE I'VE BEEN LOOKING FOR.

MR. ITAKURA, WHO MET WITH TEQUILA TWO YEARS AGO, HAS JUST DIED.

I'LL FIND THE ANSWERS TO EVERYTHING—

...AND WHAT THE MEN IN BLACK ARE TRYING TO DO.

Diary

HEY, I'VE SEEN HIM ON TV ONCE OR TWICE.

BEFORE THAT, HE WAS FAMOUS FOR CREATING CGI EFFECTS IN MOVIES.

THAT'S RIGHT. MASARU ITAKURA, AGE 45.

THE VICTIM IS A PROGRAMMER WHO DESIGNED COMPUTER GAMES?

BAKER

...BUT I DON'T SEE ANY EXTERNAL INJURIES.

WE'LL HAVE TO DO A DETAILED ANALYSIS TO KNOW FOR SURE...

AND THE CAUSE OF DEATH?

...I ESTIMATE HE'S BEEN DEAD FOR AT LEAST TWO DAYS.

FROM THE OPACITY OF HIS CORNEAS AND THE EXTENT OF RIGOR MORTIS...

...I'M GUESSING HE WAS OVERCOME BY A SUDDEN *HEART ATTACK.*

JUDGING FROM THE FACT THAT MR. ITA- KURA TOOK CORONARY DILATORS...

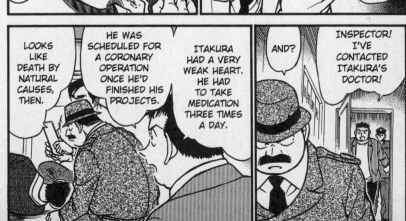

LOOKS LIKE DEATH BY NATURAL CAUSES, THEN.

HE WAS SCHEDULED FOR A CORONARY OPERATION ONCE HE'D FINISHED HIS PROJECTS.

ITAKURA HAD A VERY WEAK HEART. HE HAD TO TAKE MEDICATION THREE TIMES A DAY.

AND?

INSPECTOR! I'VE CONTACTED ITAKURA'S DOCTOR!

HEH... GUESS NOT.

...SLEEPING MOORE.

GUESS WE WON'T NEED *YOU* THIS TIME...

AND HE ONLY LIKED TO CHANGE HIS SHEETS ONCE EVERY SIX MONTHS. HE PROBABLY KEPT THAT "DO NOT DISTURB" SIGN ON HIS DOOR AROUND THE CLOCK.

ONCE HE FLIPPED OUT AT ME BECAUSE HE THOUGHT THE PAPERS ON HIS DESK HAD MOVED A COUPLE OF INCHES.

HE HATED HAVING PEOPLE IN HIS WORKSPACE.

A MAID SHOULD'VE COME BY TO MAKE HIS BED...

BUT IF HE'S BEEN DEAD FOR TWO DAYS, WHY DIDN'T THE HOTEL STAFF NOTICE?

EXECUTIVES FROM GAME COMPANIES ITAKURA WAS WORKING FOR.

WHO ARE THESE GUYS?

BUT HE LOCKED HIMSELF AWAY IN A DIRTY, UNHEALTHY ENVIRONMENT EVEN THOUGH HE KNEW HE HAD A BAD HEART. HE BROUGHT IT ON HIMSELF.

DIRTY? ARE YOU SURE?

WELL, NO.

NOT FAST ENOUGH TO SAVE HIS LIFE, THOUGH.

THEY HIRED ME TO LOOK FOR ITAKURA BECAUSE HE'D BEEN MISSING FOR A WEEK. THANKS TO MY AMAZING DEDUCTIONS, WE DISCOVERED THIS PLACE AT *LIGHTNING SPEED!*

...BUT THE DESKTOP WAS DRY!

WHEN WE CAME INTO THIS ROOM, HE WAS FACE DOWN AT THE DESK...

HUH?

I THINK HE LIKED TO KEEP THINGS *REALLY* CLEAN.

NO DROOL MARKS!

HUH?

DUMB KID!! WHY WOULD A GUY IN THE THROES OF A *HEART ATTACK* STOP TO CLEAN OFF HIS DESK?

THEN WHO CLEANED IT?

HE MUST'VE WIPED THE DESK CLEAN!

LOOK AT ALL THE DROOL ON HIS FACE!

IF THAT'S TRUE, THERE'S SOMETHING FUNNY HERE!

OH, HE FELL WHEN I SHOOK HIM!

YOU DIDN'T TELL ME YOU FOUND ITAKURA FACE DOWN AT THE DESK.

ER... I DON'T KNOW...

THEN MAYBE ITAKURA DIED SOMEWHERE ELSE...

BUT I DON'T SEE ANY PRESSURE MARKS ON HIS HANDS.

HIS HANDS ARE LOCKED TIGHTLY AGAINST HIS CHEST DUE TO RIGOR MORTIS. IF HE'D BEEN LEANING ON THE DESK ALL THIS TIME, THEY'D HAVE BEEN PRESSED AGAINST THE DESK.

THE CORPSE'S HANDS!

...AND IF HE HADN'T BEEN SITTING IN THE CHAIR, HIS LEGS WOULDN'T HAVE BEEN BENT!

IF HIS HANDS HADN'T BEEN PRESSED AGAINST THE DESK, HIS ARMS WOULD'VE FALLEN TO HIS SIDES...

BUT HIS HANDS AND LEGS ARE COMPLETELY RIGID IN THIS POSITION!

THAT'S WHY HE COULDN'T REACH HIS MEDICINE IN TIME.

I SEE... ITAKURA WAS TIED TO THE CHAIR WITH HIS HANDS AGAINST HIS CHEST.

AHA...

OH?

UNLESS YOU THINK SOMEBODY TIED HIM TO THE CHAIR IN THAT POSITION...

SOMETHING WE KNOW ALL TOO WELL.

YOU THINK THIS IS...?

NO WAY... NO...

MURDER.

...BUT THERE ARE FAINT BLOOD STASIS MARKS AROUND HIS SHOULDERS AND KNEES, AS IF HIS BODY HAD BEEN CONSTRICTED THERE.

THERE AREN'T ANY CLEAR MARKINGS...

HAVE YOU FOUND ANYTHING LIKE THAT?

BUT IF THAT'S TRUE, THERE OUGHT TO BE *ROPE MARKS* ON THE BODY.

THE BLANKET!!

I'VE GOT IT!

DON'T TOUCH THAT, CONAN!

...

HEY, IT'S KINDA STICKY IN PLACES...

OOH... THIS BLANKET IS SO SOFT AND WARM!

POOF

WHAT DOES THAT MEAN?

TO MAKE IT WORK, THE CHAIR WOULD HAVE TO HAVE BEEN FIXED TO THE DESK.

I SEE! THAT WOULDN'T LEAVE ANY ROPE MARKS ON THE BODY!

A PILLOW WAS PLACED BETWEEN HIS CHEST AND KNEES SO HIS BODY WOULD TAKE THE SHAPE OF THE DESK!

THE MURDERER WRAPPED ITAKURA'S BODY IN THE BLANKET, SAT HIM IN THE CHAIR, THEN HELD HIM IN PLACE WITH DUCT TAPE OR SOMETHING SIMILAR!

LATER, AFTER ITAKURA HAD DIED OF A HEART ATTACK AND HIS BODY HAD STARTED TO STIFFEN, THE KILLER RETURNED, REMOVED THE DUCT TAPE AND PADDING, AND TURNED HIS BODY AGAINST THE DESK TO MAKE THE DEATH LOOK NATURAL!

SO THE KILLER DRUGGED ITAKURA, TAPED HIM TO THE CHAIR, TAPED THE CHAIR TO THE DESK AND LEFT.

IT SEEMS TO HAVE BEEN WIPED OFF, BUT I CAN SEE TRACES OF DUCT TAPE ADHESIVE ON THE DESK.

HMM...

YES, SIR!!

QUESTION THE HOTEL STAFF!! ASK THEM IF ANY SUSPICIOUS-LOOKING PEOPLE HAVE VISITED IN THE LAST FEW DAYS!!

SO...WHEN I SAID THAT, THE CLERK ON THE OTHER END STARTED LAUGHING...

SO?

I TOLD THEM I WAS THE ONE WHO'D BORROWED SHOGI, CHESS AND GO SETS FROM THE FRONT DESK, AND THE PHONE IN MY ROOM WASN'T WORKING.

I FOUND THIS ROOM BY CALLING THE HOTEL AND PRETENDING TO BE ITAKURA.

WHAT?

BUT THAT'D TAKE A *BRILLIANT DEDUCTIVE MIND* TO RIVAL MY OWN! WHAT ARE THE ODDS?

THEN SOMEBODY ELSE USED THE SAME TRICK TO FIND THIS ROOM!

W H A T ?

...AND SAID, "AGAIN?"

NEVER MIND.

A FEW DAYS AGO, SOMEBODY CLAIMING TO BE ITAKURA CALLED THE HOTEL DESK AND SAID THE PHONE IN HIS ROOM WASN'T WORKING!

INSPEC- TOR!

SO HOW'D YOU KNOW ITAKURA HAD BORROWED A BUNCH OF BOARD GAMES FROM THE HOTEL?

I THINK IT'S SAFE TO SAY THAT WAS THE MURDERER.

THE VOICE ON THE PHONE WAS A MAN'S, BUT IT SOUNDED KIND OF *MUFFLED.*

WHEN A CLERK WENT TO MR. ITAKURA'S ROOM, HE SHOOED HER AWAY, SAYING, "IT WASN'T ME!"

HIS EMAIL.

THAT MEANS ...

I SEE.

IN THE PHOTO, HE WAS SITTING AT HIS CHAIR IN THE HOTEL ROOM WITH SHOGI, CHESS AND GO BOARDS IN FRONT OF HIM!

ITAKURA SENT THOSE THREE AN EMAIL WITH A PHOTO ATTACH- MENT.

...ANY ONE OF YOU COULD'VE USED THE SAME METHOD MOORE USED TO FIND ITAKURA!

HMPH.

GOOD POINT!

WHAT KIND OF MURDERER WOULD COME BACK TO THE SCENE OF THE CRIME WITH A *MASTER SLEUTH?*

WE'RE THE ONES WHO HIRED MR. MOORE IN THE FIRST PLACE!!

HANG ON A MINUTE! WE'RE INNOCENT!

...

DO YOU?

DO YOU HAVE ANY *PROOF* WE WERE HERE?

HUH?

I'VE GOT AN IDEA!

HEY!

NOW'S MY CHANCE!

BDMP

WHY DON'T YOU LOOK AT THE *DIARY* IN HIS BAG?

THAT'S MR. ITA-KURA'S, RIGHT?

MAYBE HE WROTE ABOUT THE PEOPLE WHO VISITED HIM!!

IT DOES SAY "DIARY"...

HUH?

IF I WERE THE KILLER...

JUST LOAD IT ONTO THE LAPTOP ON THE DESK!

...BUT HOW AM I SUPPOSED TO READ THIS THING?

...I'D HAVE GOTTEN RID OF EVIDENCE LIKE THIS.

IT LOOKS LIKE ITAKURA HAS BEEN KEEPING A DAILY JOURNAL FOR THE PAST FIVE YEARS.

ALL RIGHT!

PIP

AH, HERE IT IS!

VOOP

KLIK

...IS ON THAT DISK!!!

AN ACCOUNT OF THE DAY TEQUILA VISITED ITAKURA...

IT'S THERE!!

"ONE OF THOSE THREE GUYS MAY HAVE FIGURED OUT WHERE I'M STAYING.

"THE HOTEL STAFF SAID SOMETHING WEIRD TO ME TODAY.

THREE DAYS AGO!

HERE'S THE MOST RECENT ENTRY!

"OH WELL... GUESS I'LL HAVE TO CHANGE HOTELS."

YES!

UM... OKAY...

THEN I'LL PUT IT BACK IN THE BAG FOR YOU!

PIP

ISN'T THERE ANYTHING ELSE?

NO.

LOOKS LIKE HE WAS ONTO YOU THREE.

IF THEY TAKE IT DOWN TO THE POLICE STATION, I'LL **NEVER** GET A LOOK AT IT!!

RIGHT! WE MIGHT FIND EVIDENCE IN THE OTHER ENTRIES!

LET'S SEND THIS DOWN TO THE CRIME LAB AND HAVE IT CHECKED OUT.

SHF

ACK!

...BUT I HAVE **NO CLUE** WHICH OF THOSE GUYS IS THE MURDERER!

I'VE GOT TO SOLVE THIS CASE RIGHT NOW AND CONVINCE THE COPS THEY DON'T NEED THAT DISK...

...AND SOMA HIRED HIM TO CREATE A SHOGI GAME.

...SUGAI WANTED A GO GAME...

ALL I KNOW IS THAT NAITO HIRED ITAKURA TO MAKE A CHESS GAME...

...

THERE'S A BLOOD STASIS MARK ON HIS LEFT ANKLE, WHERE HIS SOCK WAS.

THE VICTIM'S ANKLE!

LOOK AT THIS!

OKAY, **THINK.** I MUST'VE OVERLOOKED SOMETHING... SOME VITAL CLUE...

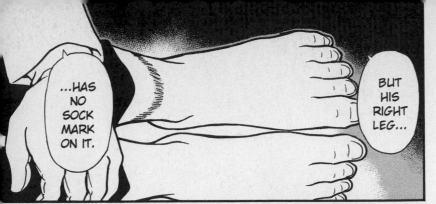

...HAS NO SOCK MARK ON IT.

BUT HIS RIGHT LEG...

...IT MUST'VE BEEN PUT ON HIS FOOT AFTER HE'D DIED AND HIS BLOOD HAD STOPPED FLOWING.

IF HIS RIGHT SOCK DIDN'T LEAVE A MARK...

HUH?

DUNNO...

WHAT DO YOU MAKE OF THAT?

...TO MAKE THE BODY LOOK NATURAL.

THE SOCK CAME OFF FOR SOME REASON, AND THE MURDERER PUT IT BACK ON...

...DID HE TAKE HIS SOCK OFF?

WHY...

BUT ITAKURA WAS TAPED TO THE CHAIR.

I KNOW WHO KILLED ITA-KURA.

I'VE GOT IT.

I SEE. ITAKURA WANTED TO LEAVE *THIS*.

...I CAN GET THAT DIARY TOO!

AND IF I ACT FAST ...

YES, SIR.

...GO AHEAD WITH THE JUDICIAL AUTOPSY!

CORONER...

YES, SIR!

TAKAGI, TAKE THE VICTIM'S DIARY DOWN TO THE CRIME LAB.

Diary

AND I'M SOMA! HE WAS MAKING A SHOGI GAME FOR *MY* COMPANY!

I'M NAITO! MY COMPANY HIRED HIM FOR A CHESS GAME!

I'M SUGAI! MY COMPANY HIRED HIM TO DESIGN A GO GAME!

YOU'VE GOT IT WRONG! WE'RE NOT FROM THE SAME COMPANY!

NOW I'VE GOT TO FIGURE OUT WHAT TO DO WITH YOU THREE GUYS FROM THE COMPANY THAT HIRED ITAKURA...

I'LL HAVE TO ASK ALL OF YOU TO VISIT THE STATION LATER. YOU TOO, MOORE.

WELL... IT LOOKS LIKE ITAKURA WAS MURDERED, BUT WE DON'T HAVE ENOUGH EVIDENCE TO HOLD ANY OF YOU.

HEY, CAN I LEAVE TOO?

...

MAY WE LEAVE? WE CAME HERE TO CONFRONT ITAKURA, BUT WE OBVIOUSLY CAN'T DO THAT NOW...

AFTER ALL, I DON'T WANT TO LET THE KILLER ESCAPE.

WHO—

THAT WASN'T ME!

HUH?

ON SECOND THOUGHT, I THINK I'LL HANG AROUND.

I'LL HEAD HOME RIGHT NOW AND—

GREAT! I'VE GOT TO CHECK UP ON THE TV SHOW I'M TAPING!

PS SH

...IN THIS HOTEL ROOM.

NOT WHEN HE'S RIGHT HERE...

POK

...BECAUSE *YOU'RE* SUCH A CLUMSY DETECTIVE.

WHAT?

RIGHT NOW HE'S DANCING WITH GLEE, JUST LIKE THIS...

BO OF

FAIR ENOUGH. I ASSUME YOU KNOW...

HEY, DAD! BE POLITE!

PULL YOURSELF TOGETHER, MR. MOORE!

SHOOP

...SO HE WOULDN'T BE ABLE TO REACH HIS HEART MEDICINE IN TIME TO SAVE HIS OWN LIFE!

...WHO WRAPPED ITAKURA IN THE BLANKET, SAT HIM IN THE CHAIR, TIED HIM DOWN WITH DUCT TAPE AND LEFT HIM THERE...

YOU'RE NOT GOING TO TELL ME YOU HEARD *A DEAD MAN SPEAK*, ARE YOU?

OH YEAH?

OF COURSE. THE LATE MR. ITAKURA TOLD ME HIMSELF.

ITAKURA'S RIGHT FOOT IS MISSING THE MARK FROM HIS SOCK.

YOU SAW IT TOO, DIDN'T YOU?

NO, I SAW HIS *ANKLE.*

NO IDEA. WHY?

SO WHY DID ITAKURA TAKE HIS SOCK OFF?

WHEN THE MURDERER CAME BACK TO THE ROOM AFTER ITAKURA HAD DIED...

...HE NOTICED THAT ONE OF ITA-KURA'S SOCKS HAD COME OFF. HE PUT IT BACK ON THE CORPSE'S FOOT.

...TO PLACE THE PIECES ON THE BOARD.

BECAUSE HE HAD TO USE HIS *TOES...*

YOU MEAN...

OH!

WHAT PIECES?

HE USED THE TOES ON HIS RIGHT FOOT TO PICK UP THE STONES...

RIGHT. ITAKURA KNEW HE DIDN'T HAVE MUCH TIME.

...THE GO STONES?

...AND SPELL OUT A DYING MESSAGE!!

IT JUST LOOKS LIKE A GO GAME.

BUT WHAT DOES IT SAY?

THIS IS A MESSAGE?

WHAT DOES THIS HAVE TO DO WITH THE GO BOARD?

ONCE YOU GET THE DISKS, INSPECTOR, SIT DOWN IN FRONT OF THE LAPTOP!

OKAY...

DETECTIVE TAKAGI! PLEASE GIVE MR. MEGUIRE THE DISK WITH THE DIARY AND AN UNOPENED FLOPPY DISK FROM ITAKURA'S BAG!

I'LL EXPLAIN IT WITH YOUR HELP, INSPECTOR.

OH, INSPEC-TOR!

WHERE?

YOU WANT ME TO *KICK* IT?

KLAK

BOOT UP?

JUST BOOT UP THE LAPTOP!

I'LL EXPLAIN LATER.

COPY THE DATA ONTO THE BLANK DISK!

...AND DRAG IT ONTO THE DESK-TOP.

NEXT, OPEN THE DIARY...

ER... OF COURSE! I KNEW THAT!

TO "BOOT UP" A COMPUTER MEANS TO *TURN IT ON!*

VOOP

KLIK

LIKE THIS!

LOOK, HE JUST WANTS YOU TO MAKE A COPY OF THE DIARY!

...COPY?

OPEN

...DRAG...

KLIK

HA! EVEN THE FANCIEST APPLI-ANCE...

DON'T HELP HIM, DETECTIVE TAKAGI.

WAIT! THAT'S --

HMPH! EVEN I CAN DO THAT...

HUH?

KLIK KLIK

NOW PLEASE TURN OFF THE COMPUT-ER!

YOU'RE JUST DOING THIS TO POKE FUN AT MY...MY LIMITED TECH SKILLS.

YOU CAN'T DO THAT!! IF YOU UNPLUG THE COMPUTER WHILE IT'S STILL ON, YOU CAN LOSE DATA OR PERMANENTLY DAMAGE THE HARD DRIVE!!

HUH?

NOOO!!

...CAN BE TURNED OFF BY *PULLING THE PLUG!!*

POP

IT'S DESIGNED THAT WAY FOR SAFETY REASONS. YOU HAVE TO HOLD THE POWER BUTTON DOWN.

BUT IT WOULDN'T TURN OFF WHEN I PRESSED THE BUTTON...

...AND ONLY A PERSON WHO KNOWS COMPUTERS CAN UNDERSTAND TERMS LIKE "BOOT" OR "DRAG."

RIGHT... ANYONE WHO KNOWS COMPUTERS KNOWS IT'S TABOO TO UNPLUG IT...

LOOK!

HEY, THAT BOARD IS A MESS!

WHAT?

HUH...

DO *YOU?*

NOW DO YOU KNOW WHAT THE GO STONES SAY?

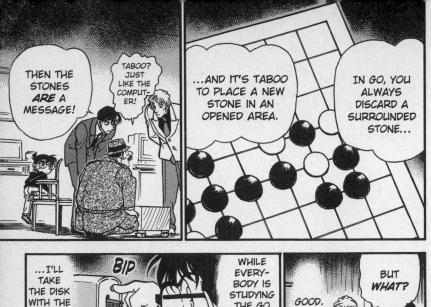

THEN THE STONES *ARE* A MESSAGE!

TABOO? JUST LIKE THE COMPUTER!

...AND IT'S TABOO TO PLACE A NEW STONE IN AN OPENED AREA.

IN GO, YOU ALWAYS DISCARD A SURROUNDED STONE...

...I'LL TAKE THE DISK WITH THE COPY OF THE DIARY...

BIP

POK

BDMP

WHILE EVERYBODY IS STUDYING THE GO BOARD...

GOOD.

BUT *WHAT?*

PIP

BDMP

BDMP

I...I WAS JUST THINKING THOSE GO STONES REMINDED ME OF SOMETHING.

THEN WHAT ARE YOU DOING?

NO! NOTHING!

HEY, ARE YOU HIDING SOMETHING FROM ME?

YIPE

WHAT'RE YOU DOING, CONAN?

...STUCK ON THE KEY-BOARD!

THESE STICKERS WITH THE FUNNY PATTERNS...

BRAILLE?

HE TOLD ME HE WAS STARTING TO LEARN BRAILLE.

COME TO THINK OF IT, ITAKURA HAD BAD EYESIGHT LIKE ME.

OH, I SEE. THAT'S BRAILLE, CONAN.

WHAT?

MAYBE THIS IS WRITTEN IN BRAILLE!

I SEE! WORDS ONLY THOSE IN THE KNOW CAN UNDER-STAND!

...MUR...

...DER...

...ER...

...E....

TH...

OH! BUT IF I SKIP THE WHITE STONES, IT SPELLS OUT JAPANESE BRAILLE CHARAC-TERS!

I DON'T THINK THERE ARE ANY SHAPES LIKE THESE IN BRAILLE...

IS IT?

...HE KNEW THE MURDERER WOULD HAVE TO COME BACK TO ARRANGE HIS BODY AND REMOVE THE EVIDENCE OF FOUL PLAY.

OKAY. WHEN ITAKURA LEFT THIS DYING MESSAGE...

CALM DOWN... CALM DOWN...

I ALREADY HAVE THE DIARY IN MY HANDS.

WHEW...

BDMP BDMP

AFTER ALL, IF SOMA SUSPECTED THE GO BOARD CONTAINED A MESSAGE, HE'D GET RID OF IT.

SO HE CREATED A *SECRET CODE* HE KNEW SOMA WOULDN'T BE ABLE TO READ.

...AND FIGURE OUT THERE WAS A SECRET CODE FOR THE POLICE TO DECIPHER!

...OR ELSE SUGAI, WHO HAD HIRED ITAKURA TO CREATE THE GO GAME, WOULD REALIZE THE LAYOUT OF THE BOARD WAS WRONG...

WHEN THAT HAPPENED, NAITO, WHO HAS SUCH BAD EYESIGHT THAT HE HAS TO USE THE BRAILLE ON ELEVATOR BUTTONS, WOULD BE ABLE TO DECIPHER THE GO CODE...

PIP

...AND THE POLICE WOULD PROBABLY SHOW YOU PHOTOS OF THE CRIME SCENE!

ITAKURA KNEW THAT ONCE HIS BODY WAS FOUND, ALL THREE OF YOU WOULD BE UNDER SUSPICION...

HE LIKES FANCY WATCHES, AND HE HAS VERY BAD EYESIGHT.

ITAKURA MOVED INTO THIS ROOM ABOUT A WEEK AGO.

IT'S THE WATCH SOMA'S WEARING RIGHT NOW.

BUT WHAT'S THIS ABOUT A WATCH?

I SEE!

...THAT EXPENSIVE WATCH YOU BOUGHT FIVE DAYS AGO!

WHEN YOU FIRST CAME TO VISIT HIM AT THIS HOTEL, I BET HE GRABBED YOUR HAND AND TOUCHED...

I'M SURE HIS PRINTS ARE ALL OVER THIS THING.

SURE, TAKE A GOOD LOOK.

I'M SENDING THIS WATCH DOWN TO THE LAB!

RIGHT... IF THIS IS *REALLY* THE FIRST TIME YOU'VE SEEN ITAKURA SINCE HE DISAPPEARED, HIS PRINTS COULDN'T POSSIBLY BE ON THE WATCH.

I SEE! IF ITAKURA'S FINGER-PRINTS ARE ON THE WATCH, IT'LL BE SOLID PROOF!

...AND HE STILL HAD IT IN HIS HANDS WHEN I WRAPPED HIM IN THE BLANKET.

I LET HIM FIDDLE WITH THIS WATCH WHILE I DRUGGED HIS WINE...

BUT THREE DAYS AGO, WHEN I TRACKED HIM DOWN AND VISITED HIM AT THIS HOTEL, HE ASKED ME...

OUR BIG DREAM WAS TO CREATE A COMPUTER PROGRAM THAT COULD DEFEAT EVEN A SHOGI GRAND MASTER. I NEVER LOST THAT DREAM.

AFTER PRACTICE, WE'D TALK SHOGI OVER DRINKS.

...WE WERE SHOGI BUDDIES AT THE SAME TRAINING ACADEMY.

TWENTY YEARS AGO, WHEN HE WAS A NO-NAME PROGRAMMER AND I WAS JUST GETTING STARTED IN THE GAME INDUSTRY...

AND HE WANTED TO ADD *TAKE-BACK MOVES!*

WHAT KIND OF JOKE IS THAT? I THOUGHT HE WAS SERIOUS ABOUT BUILDING A MASTER-CLASS GAME! I'D BEEN SENDING HIM RECORDS OF GREAT SHOGI MATCHES OF THE PAST 20 YEARS! TAKING HEAVY LOANS TO FINANCE THE PROJECT OUT OF MY OWN POCKET!

..."HOW MANY TIMES SHOULD THE PLAYER BE ALLOWED TO TAKE BACK A MOVE?"

...AND STEPPED OUT TO BUY *WINE, DUCT TAPE* AND *SLEEPING PILLS.*

SO I TOLD HIM I'D GET US A BOTTLE OF WINE TO CELEBRATE...

OUR DREAMS CHANGED TOO MUCH.

I GUESS WE DRIFTED APART IN THOSE 20 YEARS.

AFTER ALL, I'D BEEN COMPLAINING ABOUT HIS DISAPPEARANCE MORE THAN ANYONE! EVERY-BODY AT THE OFFICE KNEW I WAS MAD AT HIM FOR DELAYING THE SHOGI GAME AND SWANNING AROUND ON TV TALK SHOWS!

WHEN YOU GUYS CAME TO ME ABOUT HIRING A PRIVATE EYE TO FIND ITAKURA, I HAD TO GO ALONG SO I WOULDN'T LOOK SUSPICIOUS.

BACK TO WHEN WE BOTH HAD THE SAME DREAMS ...

IF WE COULD HAVE TAKE-BACK MOVES IN *LIFE,* I'D GO BACK TO 20 YEARS AGO.

TAKE CARE, RACHEL!

IT'S HERE!

I'VE GOT IT WITH ME!

DON'T WORRY! IT'S JUST A HALF-HOUR WALK HOME!

YOU AND CONAN CATCH A TAXI HOME! YOUR FATHER AND I NEED TO TALK A LITTLE!

YAWN

BYE-BYE, INSPECTOR!

THE EVIDENCE THAT COULD LEAD ME TO THE MEN IN BLACK!!

IT'S IN MY POCKET!

GRP

BDMP

HEY, CONAN.

...AND READ EVERY WORD OF THIS DIARY...

I'LL DROP BY DR. AGASA'S HOUSE LATER...

BDMP

BDMP

OH, CONAN...

I WISH YOU WERE HIM...

RACHEL... NO...

WHAT AM I SAYING?

SILLY ME!

I HAVE TO TELL HER...

I...

THEN I'LL TELL HER EVERYTHING—

NOT UNTIL I *CRUSH* THEM!

NOT UNTIL I FIND OUT WHO THEY ARE!

NO!! I CAN'T!

YOU'RE CRYING AGAIN.

FILE 8: WHITE SNOW, BLACK SHADOW

ALWAYS CRYING, AREN'T YOU?

WHAT?

"AGAIN"?

HUH?

HYOO

GOT A PROBLEM WITH THAT?

NAH.

WHAT?

WHAT?

I WAS JUST THINK-ING...

...YOU REMIND ME OF A WOMAN I KNOW.

TOK

TOK

...WHO PUT UP A TOUGH FRONT BUT CRIED BEHIND MY BACK.

A STUPID WOMAN...

TOK

TOK

TOK

YEAH. I MET HIM IN NEW YORK A WHILE BACK.

RACHEL!! DO YOU KNOW THAT MAN?

IS HE CALLING ME STUPID?

...AND ASKED ME IF I'D SEEN A JAPANESE GUY WITH LONG SILVER HAIR.

HE CAME UP TO ME WHILE I WAS WAITING FOR JIMMY IN FRONT OF AN OLD BUILDING...

HUH?

HE WAS WITH A GUY IN A JACKET WITH "FBI" PRINTED ON THE BACK.

HE'S KINDA CREEPY, BUT I THINK HE'S AN OKAY GUY.

THE NIGHT I WENT AFTER THE SLASHER!!

THAT'S CRAZY! WHY WOULD THE FBI...

...BE HERE IN JAPAN?

FBI?

VANISHED INTO THIN AIR...

HE'S GONE!

IF THE FBI HAD BEEN IN THE AREA, THEY NEVER WOULD'VE LET THAT HAPPEN.

SOMEBODY KILLED THE SLASHER AND MADE IT LOOK LIKE A SUICIDE.

IS THAT GUY REALLY WITH THE FBI?

LET'S GET HOME, CONAN!

UM, OKAY...

WHAT IF HE'S CONNECTED TO THE MEN IN BLACK?

WHAT IF HE WAS THE ONE WHO KILLED THE SLASHER?

AND ANITA REACTED TO HIS PRESENCE WHEN JAMES BLACK WAS KIDNAPPED.

...SHUICHI AKAI?

WHO IS...

I KNOW IT'S BEEN A WHILE, BUT I'VE INVENTED SOMETHING NEW FOR YOU!!

AH, JIMMY! PERFECT TIMING!!

HEY!

I WON'T HAVE YOU PEEPING ON HER!

NOW, HOLD ON!

PERFECT.

TAKING A BATH.

...IN CASE YOUR BATTERY RUNS OUT--

AND LOOK! I MADE YOU A SPARE PAIR OF GLASSES...

WHERE'S ANITA?

PAF

YOU'VE GOT A LEAD?

THIS IS IT!!

...TWO YEARS...

OKAY, TWO YEARS AGO...

...SO I WANT TO READ THIS WHILE SHE'S NOT AROUND.

YEAH. IF ANITA FINDS OUT, SHE'LL HAVE ANOTHER PANIC ATTACK...

REALLY, JIMMY?

KLIK

KLIK

December 19
A friend I haven't seen for five years just called from my vacation house. Apparently he's spending the night there with some girl. What a self-centered idiot.

I'm so tired.
This is going to be
the death of me.

December 20
I had to go to the bank today to make a

?!

YOU JUST TYPE THE WORDS USING THE SAME COLOR AS THE BACKGROUND!

PEOPLE OFTEN USE THIS ON WEBSITES TO CREATE HIDDEN TEXT.

JUST LIKE INVISIBLE INK!

THERE'S SOMETHING WRITTEN IN WHITE LETTERS!

↓ Spoilers below!
The truth is, he's in plain

HE SEEMS TO HAVE STARTED USING IT TEN DAYS AFTER THE BIG GUY STOPPED BY HIS OFFICE.

LET'S KEEP READING.

KUK

HE MUST'VE BELIEVED SOMEONE WAS READING HIS DIARY. HE CAME UP WITH THIS AS CAMOUFLAGE.

KUK

BUT WHY WOULD ITAKURA DO SOMETHING LIKE THIS?

"JANUARY 6. I GIVE UP. I LEFT A MESSAGE IN MY DESK FOR THE INTRUDER. IT SAYS, 'I'LL DO WHATEVER YOU SAY.'"

"DECEMBER 19. I'M SO TIRED. THIS IS GOING TO BE THE DEATH OF ME."

"JULY 6. WHO ARE YOU? SHOW YOURSELF!!"

"JUNE 11. I CHANGED THE LOCKS AND INSTALLED SURVEILLANCE CAMERAS, BUT NOTHING WORKS."

"APRIL 15. THEY ENTERED MY HOUSE THIS TIME. THE POLICE WON'T LISTEN TO ME. I GUESS I CAN'T BLAME THEM SINCE NOTHING'S GONE MISSING AND I DON'T HAVE ANY PROOF OF A BREAK-IN."

"MARCH 26. THE PAPERS ON MY DESK MOVED TWO INCHES AGAIN. JUST AS I THOUGHT-- SOMEBODY'S BEEN BREAKING INTO MY OFFICE."

"JANUARY 23. AFTER A LOT OF THOUGHT, I DECIDED NOT TO GO TO THE POLICE. I CALLED THE NUMBER.

"THE LETTERS LOOK LIKE THEY WERE WRITTEN IN BLOOD. ARE THEY TRYING TO TELL ME I'LL BE KILLED IF I TALK?"

"JUST A PHONE NUMBER UNDER THE LETTERS 'OK.'

"JANUARY 8. THE REPLY CAME QUICKLY. THE INTRUDER TOOK MY MESSAGE AND LEFT A NOTE IN ITS PLACE.

"IT SOUNDS LIKE SHE AND THE BIG GUY WHO VISITED ME A WHILE BACK ARE IN THIS TOGETHER."

"SHE WANTED ME TO COMPLETE THAT PROGRAM I WAS DEVELOPING A WHILE BACK. SHE SAID IF I FINISHED IT IN A YEAR, THEY'D PAY ME A HUGE SUM.

"A WOMAN ANSWERED. SHE SOUNDED HAUGHTY, LIKE A QUEEN OR SOMETHING.

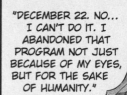

"DECEMBER 22. NO... I CAN'T DO IT. I ABANDONED THAT PROGRAM NOT JUST BECAUSE OF MY EYES, BUT FOR THE SAKE OF HUMANITY."

"FEBRUARY 13. WE'RE NOW COMMUNICATING EXCLUSIVELY OVER EMAIL. I AGREED TO FINISH WORK ON THE SOFTWARE UNDER TWO CONDITIONS: I GET PAID UP FRONT, AND THEY LEAVE ME ALONE."

"AN EMAIL GIVING ME THE TIME AND PLACE OF OUR FINAL MEETING WILL ARRIVE IN MY INBOX AT MIDNIGHT, FIVE DAYS FROM TODAY. I'VE GOT TO ESCAPE BY THEN."

"I'M GOING TO HIDE THE UNFINISHED SOFTWARE, ALONG WITH THE CHECK THEY SENT ME, NEAR THE COMPUTER AT MY VACATION HOME. THEN I'M GOING TO FLEE OVERSEAS.

"FEBRUARY 9. THE DEADLINE IS DRAWING NEAR.

WHAT DOES HE MEAN?

SAY! LOOKS LIKE THERE'S MORE HIDDEN UNDER THE LAST ENTRY!

HE WAS TRYING TO COLLECT ENOUGH MONEY TO FLEE THE COUNTRY. THE WHOLE TIME HE WAS PRETENDING TO WORK ON THE GAMES, HE WAS PLANNING HIS ESCAPE!

SO THAT'S WHY ITAKURA ACCEPTED WORK FROM THOSE THREE GAME COMPANIES.

THIS ENTRY IS DATED FOUR DAYS AGO. THE MEN IN BLACK ARE GOING TO EMAIL ITAKURA IN *THREE HOURS!*

"SHE JUST LAUGHED AND REPLIED IN ENGLISH...

"I GOT SO FED UP WITH HER ARROGANT ATTITUDE THAT I SHOUTED, 'WHO DO YOU THINK YOU ARE?'

"I CAN'T STOP THINKING ABOUT THE WORDS THAT WOMAN SAID THE FIRST TIME I CALLED THE NUMBER.

"FEBRUARY 10. WHY DO THEY WANT THAT SOFTWARE ANYWAY?

...SINCE WE'RE TRYING TO RAISE THE DEAD AGAINST THE STREAM OF TIME.'"

'YOU COULD SAY WE'RE OF BOTH GOD AND THE DEVIL...

You could say we're of both God and the Devil, since we're trying to raise the dead against the stream of time.

"...TRYING TO RAISE THE DEAD..."

"...AND THE DEVIL...

"BOTH GOD...

WHAT?

WH...

"...AGAINST THE STREAM OF TIME."

I, ER...

OH, ME?

WHAT BRINGS *YOU* HERE, JIMMY?

ER... THAT'S RIGHT! I'M A BIG FAN OF THIS ENGLISH NOVEL THAT'S BEING SERIALIZED ONLINE!

WHAT IS THAT? SOME KIND OF FANTASY NOVEL WITH WIZARDS AND WHAT-NOT?

IT'S CALLED...

UH... YEAH!

RIGHT?

HE'S HERE TO TRY OUT MY LATEST INVENTION!!

KLIK

HA HA HA!

WHOA!

BUT IF YOU TURN THE DIAL AND PRESS THE BUTTON...

NO, IT DOESN'T.

AT FIRST GLANCE, IT LOOKS LIKE ANY ORDINARY BELT!

...THE INSTANT BALL BELT!

FWEE

WOW!!

LOOK! YOU'VE GOT YOUR OWN SOCCER BALL!!

POP

SO I SEE.

THE RUBBERY MATERIAL I USE TO MAKE THE BALLS ONLY STAYS INTACT FOR ABOUT TEN SECONDS.

PSSH

NO, JUST ONE OR TWO.

WITH THIS AND THE SUPER SNEAKERS, I CAN STOP ANY NUMBER OF CROOKS!!

PSSH

TAF TAP

WHAT ELSE?

SO WHAT NOW, JIMMY?

YOU BOYS CAN PLAY WITH YOUR BALLS.

I'M GOING TO BED.

NOW *THAT'S* COOL!!

BUT IT'S EXTREMELY ELASTIC! YOU CAN INFLATE A BALL TO THE SIZE OF A *PARADE BALLOON!!*

IT'LL TELL US WHERE TO MEET THE MEN IN BLACK!

...AND PICK UP THE EMAIL HE'S SUP-POSED TO RECEIVE AT MID-NIGHT!

WE'RE GOING TO ITAKURA'S VACATION HOUSE TO FIND THAT SOFT-WARE...

WHAT IF THEY'RE LYING IN WAIT FOR HIM?

ARE YOU SURE THIS IS A GOOD IDEA, JIMMY?

...THEY GAVE HIM A LIST OF ADDRESSES WHERE HE MIGHT BE HIDING.

WHEN THOSE GUYS FROM THE GAME COMPANIES HIRED MR. MOORE TO FIND ITAKURA...

HOW'D YOU KNOW THE HOUSE WAS IN GUNMA?

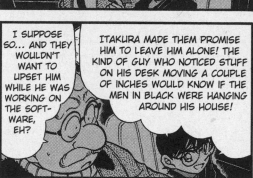

I SUPPOSE SO... AND THEY WOULDN'T WANT TO UPSET HIM WHILE HE WAS WORKING ON THE SOFT-WARE, EH?

ITAKURA MADE THEM PROMISE HIM TO LEAVE HIM ALONE! THE KIND OF GUY WHO NOTICED STUFF ON HIS DESK MOVING A COUPLE OF INCHES WOULD KNOW IF THE MEN IN BLACK WERE HANGING AROUND HIS HOUSE!

VROOM

RIGHT...

AND THOSE WEIRD LINES FROM ITAKURA'S LAST ENTRY BUG ME.

BUT THE NEWS ABOUT ITAKURA WILL PROBABLY BREAK TOMOR-ROW.

WE SHOULD BE SAFE FOR NOW! ALL THE NEWS OUT-LETS HAVE BEEN COVERING SOME BIG JEWEL HEIST!

THE THREE SUSPECTS ARE STILL AT LARGE...

BUT IF THE NEWS HAS GOTTEN OUT THAT ITAKURA IS DEAD...

WE'RE NOT TALKING ABOUT *ZOMBIES* HERE!

NOW, NOW, JIMMY!

HEY, DOC! YOU DON'T THINK THE DRUG ANITA WAS WORKING ON WAS...?

"...SINCE WE'RE TRYING TO RAISE THE DEAD AGAINST THE STREAM OF TIME."

"YOU COULD SAY WE'RE OF BOTH GOD AND THE DEVIL...

MAN CANNOT HALT THE FLOW OF TIME.

DON'T BLOW YOUR TOP.

...

WHAT KIND OF SUFFERING, ANITA?

WHAT?

IF YOU PERSIST IN TRYING TO THWART NATURE... YOU WILL SUFFER FOR IT.

...HOW DO WE GET IN?

NOW ...

KLIK

WHEW! MADE IT!

SKREE

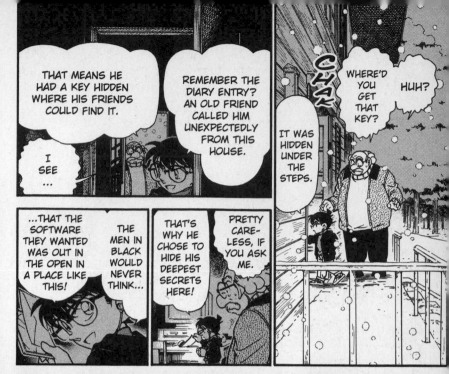

THAT MEANS HE HAD A KEY HIDDEN WHERE HIS FRIENDS COULD FIND IT.

REMEMBER THE DIARY ENTRY? AN OLD FRIEND CALLED HIM UNEXPECTEDLY FROM THIS HOUSE.

I SEE...

WHERE'D YOU GET THAT KEY?

HUH?

IT WAS HIDDEN UNDER THE STEPS.

...THAT THE SOFTWARE THEY WANTED WAS OUT IN THE OPEN IN A PLACE LIKE THIS!

THE MEN IN BLACK WOULD NEVER THINK...

THAT'S WHY HE CHOSE TO HIDE HIS DEEPEST SECRETS HERE!

PRETTY CARE- LESS, IF YOU ASK ME.

...IT'S ALMOST TIME.

WELL, JIMMY...

I KNOW.

WHEN THEY CAME OUT TO INVESTIGATE, THEY'D FIND THE UNFINISHED SOFTWARE AND THE CHECK, SO HE COULD END HIS BUSINESS WITH THEM WITHOUT MEETING THEM FACE-TO-FACE!

HE WAS PLAN- NING TO FLEE THE COUNTRY WITHOUT ANSWERING THE EMAIL THEY'RE ABOUT TO SEND.

SHOW ME YOUR DIRTY FACE!!!

LET'S SEE IT, BLACK ORGANIZ- ATION!!

FILE 9:
A DANGEROUS MEETING

...ALL ALONG.

HYOOO

...THEY'VE HAD THIS HOUSE STAKED OUT...

HEY, PICK UP THE PHONE!!

BUT IF THAT'S TRUE, WE'RE *TRAPPED*!!

I DIDN'T THINK THEY'D LET ITAKURA RECEIVE THE EMAIL AT A LOCATION THEY WEREN'T MONITORING.

WHAT?

...

PICK UP ALREADY !!

I KNOW YOU'RE THERE!

NO!

IT'S DANGEROUS, BUT WE'LL HAVE TO SNEAK OUT THE BACK DOOR IN THIS BLIZZARD!

W...WE'VE GOT NO CHOICE.

C'MON, ITA-KURA!!

CHAK

COULDN'T FIND THE PHONE IN THE DARK.

SORRY ABOUT THAT.

I HAVEN'T BEEN ABLE TO GET ONLINE AND CHECK MY EMAIL.

LOOKS LIKE THE BLIZZARD CAUSED A *BLACKOUT* HERE.

HOLD ON, JIMMY!

HA HA HA...

?

HEY, HOW'D YOU KNOW I WAS HERE?

SERVES YOU RIGHT FOR RUNNING OFF TO YOUR HOUSE IN THE MOUNTAINS.

HMPH.

Turn the light on!

HUH?

WE KNOW ALL ABOUT YOU, YOU KNOW...

PAF

KUK

HEY!

YES. IT WAS TOUGH, BUT IT'S DONE.

TAP TAP

CHILL OUT, GEEK. IT'S NOT LIKE THAT.

WE'RE GETTING OFF THE SUBJECT. YOU'VE FINISHED THAT SOFTWARE FOR US, RIGHT?

YOU HAVEN'T BEEN SPYING ON ME, HAVE YOU?

IS THERE SOMEBODY ELSE THERE?

I SEE. SNOWING PRETTY HARD OVER THERE, HUH?

TH...THE WIND. JUST THE WIND RATTLING THE WINDOWS.

KLAK KLAK

WHAT WAS THAT SOUND?

SOUND?

LISTEN CLOSE, 'CAUSE I'M ONLY GONNA SAY THIS ONCE.

YOU'RE A PIECE OF WORK, AIN'T YA?

...WHEN AND WHERE I'M SUPPOSED TO HAND OVER THIS SOFTWARE?

CAN YOU JUST TELL ME...

SO, LIKE I SAID, I CAN'T GET ONLINE RIGHT NOW.

YOU KNOW KENBASHI STATION, THE ONE THAT'S UNDER CONSTRUCTION RIGHT NOW?

IT'S GONNA BE A FANCY NEW ADDITION TO THE TOUTO SUBWAY LINE.

TOMORROW AT MIDNIGHT, GO TO LOCKER NUMBER 0032 IN THE LOWEST LEVEL OF THE STATION.

I'M SCHEDULED TO CHECK IN AT THE HOSPITAL FOR AN OPERATION. YOU KNOW ABOUT MY BAD HEART, RIGHT?

WHAT?

NO. I CAN'T MAKE IT TOMORROW.

AND DON'T FORGET THAT SOFTWARE...

...

THEN WHEN CAN YOU HAND IT OVER?

N...NOT AT ALL! IT'S READY!

HEY! YOU AIN'T TRYING TO BUY EXTRA TIME TO FINISH THAT SOFTWARE, ARE YA?

AND WE'D HAVE TO GET TO THE STATION BEFORE THE CONSTRUCTION CREWS STARTED WORK, SO THERE'S NO WAY—

I COULD GIVE YOU THE SOFTWARE, BUT IT'D HAVE TO BE TODAY.

I CAN'T DO THAT. IT TOOK ME FOREVER TO GET AN APPOINTMENT WITH A TOP HEART SURGEON.

WE AIN'T GONNA WAIT THAT LONG! RESCHEDULE YOUR OPERATION!

NOT UNTIL I'M OUT OF THE HOSPITAL. THREE OR FOUR DAYS... NO, GIVE ME AT LEAST FIVE DAYS.

WHAT'S WRONG? DON'T YOU HAVE THE SOFT- WARE?

FOUR HOURS? FROM GUNMA TO TOKYO?

COME TO THE PLACE I JUST SPECIFIED FOUR HOURS FROM NOW.

OKAY. 4 A.M.

WHAT?

BUT PROMISE ME THERE WON'T BE AN AMBUSH.

FINE, FINE. 4 A.M.

HEH... I HEARD YOU WERE A CAUTIOUS GUY.

...YOU'LL NEVER FIGURE OUT HOW TO USE IT.

IF...IF YOU TAKE THE SOFTWARE FROM ME BY FORCE...

IF I SEE EVEN ONE OF YOUR FRIENDS, THE DEAL IS OFF.

BRRR

BRRR

PIP

GOT IT.

DON'T BE LATE. LOCKER 0032 AT THE LOWEST LEVEL OF KENBASHI STATION, 4 A.M.

JIMMY, WHAT'RE YOU DOING? YOU'RE NOT GOING TO FOLLOW THEIR ORDERS AND TAKE THAT SOFTWARE TO THE STATION, ARE YOU?

I'M NOT FOLLOWING ANYBODY'S ORDERS.

THEY BOUGHT IT!!!

GOOD.

...BY PRETENDING TO BE SCARED!

I PUSHED HIM TO CHANGE THE TIME TO 4 A.M....

LUCKILY, NONE OF THE STATIONS HAVE COVERED ITAKURA'S DEATH YET.

NOW THE JEWEL THIEVES ARE ON THE RUN...

IF THAT HAPPENS, THE WHOLE DEAL'S OFF.

WHEN DAWN BREAKS, THERE'S A GOOD CHANCE THEY'LL HEAR ABOUT ITAKURA'S DEATH ON THE MORNING NEWS.

BUT WHY?

OKAY! LET'S GET RID OF ANY EVIDENCE THAT WE WERE HERE, THEN HEAD OUT IN YOUR CAR!

HEAD OUT?

OF COURSE. IF I'D BEEN ABLE TO OPEN THAT EMAIL, I WAS GOING TO SEND AN EMAIL BACK CONVINCING THEM TO CHANGE THE DATE.

YOU PLANNED THE WHOLE THING!

AND HE WOULDN'T HAVE TOLD ME WHERE TO MEET IF HE THOUGHT THERE WAS A CHANCE HIS VOICE WAS BEING RECORDED!

IF ANYONE HAD BEEN WATCHING THIS PLACE, VODKA WOULD'VE KNOWN I WAS LYING ABOUT THE BLACKOUT!

WE'RE SAFE!

IF WE GO OUTSIDE NOW, THEY'LL CATCH US IN AN INSTANT!

WHAT IF OTHER MEMBERS OF THE SYNDICATE ARE WATCHING US?

THEY PROBABLY FIGURED OUT WHERE WE ARE BECAUSE THEY'VE GOT ITAKURA'S COMPUTERS BUGGED SOMEHOW.

YEAH! IT PROVES THEY'RE NOT WITHIN SIGHT OF THIS HOUSE!

I SEE! THAT'S WHY YOU HAD ME TURN ON THE LIGHTS!

...AND GET THEM TO STAKE OUT THAT SUBWAY STATION!

YOU'LL HAND IT OVER TO THE POLICE...

IF IT'S SOMETHING THAT CAN BE USED FOR CRIME...

I'M GOING TO CHECK OUT THIS SOFTWARE ON YOUR LAPTOP IN THE CAR.

ANYWAY, THIS HAS GOT TO BRING DOWN SOME OF THE MEN IN BLACK.

IT'S NO USE!

VROOM

DARN IT!

JUST TELL THE POLICE THERE'LL BE ILLEGAL CONCEALED WEAPONS. THEY'LL TAKE *THAT* SERIOUSLY!

DON'T THE MEMBERS OF THE SYNDICATE ALWAYS CARRY GUNS?

I CAN'T. THE WHOLE THING'S COPY PROTECTED. IF I CAN'T OPEN THIS, I'LL *NEVER* GET THE POLICE TO LISTEN TO ME!!

THE SOFTWARE'S LOCKED BEHIND A PASSWORD TOO!! THEY MUST'VE TOLD ITAKURA TO PROTECT EVERYTHING WITH A PASSWORD ONLY THEY WOULD KNOW!

WELL, JUST COPY IT ONTO THE LAPTOP!

WE HAVE TO FIGURE OUT WHAT THEY'RE AFTER AND SHOW THE POLICE WE'RE UP AGAINST A LARGE, DANGEROUS ORGANIZATION. IT'S THE ONLY WAY TO GET ENOUGH BACKUP TO STOP THEM!

ONLY ENOUGH TO SEND A COP OR TWO. WE DON'T KNOW HOW MANY MEN IN BLACK WILL BE AT THE STATION.

OH?

NO... I'VE STILL GOT ONE OPTION.

WE KNOW THEY'RE GOING TO BE THERE, BUT WE CAN'T DO ANYTHING ABOUT IT!

HMM... THIS IS TOUGH.

BUT IT'S GOING TO BE A LITTLE *DANGEROUS.*

I-I'M AFRAID IT I-IS...

THUNK

THUNK

THIS HAD B-BETTER NOT BE—

H-HEY, DOC!

THUNK

JIMMY! YOU'RE NOT PLANNING TO MEET THEM *YOURSELF*, ARE YOU?

HY 0 0 0 0

JUST AS I THOUGHT! A FLAT TIRE!

I THINK IT'S A *SIGN FROM ABOVE* THAT WE SHOULDN'T RISK IT!

HUH?

BUT WE WON'T MAKE IT TO THE STATION IN TIME FOR THE DEAL!

WE'LL JUST HAVE TO WAIT FOR THEM IN THE CAR!

WE DON'T HAVE TIME! IT'LL TAKE *FOREVER* FOR THEM TO FIND US OUT HERE IN THE MIDDLE OF THE NIGHT!

WE'LL HAVE TO CONTACT THE NEAREST GAS STATION AND HAVE THEM BRING OUT A NEW TIRE.

...CAR!

A...

I DIDN'T HEAR ANYTHING.

HUH?

HEY... WHAT WAS THAT WEIRD NOISE?

YOU NEEDN'T HURRY. SAFE DRIVING, PLEASE!

THAT WAS CLOSE. THESE SNOWY ROADS ARE TREACHEROUS, HUH?

HEY! DON'T SMOKE!!

FORGET ABOUT IT.

THE LUGGAGE IN THE TRUNK MUST'VE SHIFTED.

I FORGOT.

OH! SORRY!

YOU KNOW HOW MUCH I HATE SMOKING!!

SCREE

WITH THE SNOW LETTING UP, WE SHOULD GET THERE RIGHT AROUND 3 A.M.

THANKS.

TURN LEFT THERE FOR TOKYO!

WELL, SOMETHING LIKE THAT...

NICE.

KLIK

SKI TRIP WITH YOUR GRANDSON HERE?

SO WHAT TOOK YOU TO GUNMA?

VROOOM

BEEP BEEP

HYOOO

OOPS!

...

...

I SHOULDN'T HAVE GOTTEN ON THAT ICY ROAD TO BEGIN WITH...

SORRY, SORRY!

HEY, CAN'T YOU DRIVE?

BEEP BEEP

SKREE

HYOO

WHOA!

...I DON'T LIKE DRIVING IN THE SNOW!

THIS IS WHY...

...

CARS ARE HONKING AT US!

KNOCK IT OFF!

WHEW!!

ER...
RIGHT
...

HUH?

THAT'S RIGHT,
MISTER! IT'S
ALMOST TIME
FOR THIS CAR'S
INSPECTION, SO
YOU'D BETTER
DRIVE
SAFELY!

DON'T YOU
REMEMBER?
THE STICKER
ON THE WIND-
SHIELD HAS A
NUMBER 2
ON IT!

I
GUESS
IT COULD
BE...

IT IS
ALMOST
TIME
FOR AN
INSPECTION,
RIGHT?

I GOT A
LETTER
TELLING ME
TO GET IT
INSPECTED
THIS
MONTH!

OH
YEAH! I
REMEM-
BER
NOW!!

THE STICKER
IS THIS
YEAR'S COLOR,
SO THE NEXT
INSPECTION
IS THIS
FEBRUARY!

THOSE STICKERS ARE
INSPECTION EMBLEMS. THE
NUMBER AND COLOR TELL
YOU WHEN THE CAR IS
SUPPOSED TO BE
INSPECTED!

THE HEAD-
LIGHTS FROM
THE OTHER
CAR LIGHT UP
THE NUMBER
FROM BEHIND!

LOOK! YOU
CAN SEE IT
WHEN A CAR
PASSES BY!

BUT HOW'D
YOU SPOT THAT
STICKER UNDER
THE SNOW?

HUH?

I THOUGHT IT WAS A 2, BUT I'M LOOKING AT IT BACKWARDS! IT'S ACTUALLY A 5!

OOPS, SORRY!

...

Department of Motor Vehicles

THAT'S BE-CAUSE...

OH, ER...

...

HOW COULD THAT BE?

YOU SAID YOU GOT A LETTER TELLING YOU TO GET THE CAR INSPECTED THIS MONTH.

BUT THAT'S FUNNY.

OH!

HE DOESN'T KNOW ANYTHING ABOUT HIS CAR'S MAINTENANCE! HE WAS JUST ANSWERING YOU TO BE POLITE!

HE HAS *PEOPLE* TO HANDLE THAT STUFF FOR HIM!

HE MADE IT ALL UP! HE'S A RICH BRAT, REMEMBER?

SKREE

WHAT?

YOU WERE SUPPOSED TO MAKE A RIGHT TURN BACK THERE!

HM...

AH...

SORRY! HE'S A VERY CURIOUS BOY!

FORGET ABOUT IT.

YOUR GRAND-SON'S DIS-TRACTING ME.

TCH...

THE ECONOMIC RECOVERY, BIG OSAKA'S NEW COACH...

UH-HUH! THEY'VE BEEN TALKING ABOUT LOTS OF THINGS!

NEWS?

THE NEWS ON THE RADIO!

OH, THIS?

BY THE WAY, LITTLE BOY, WHAT'RE YOU LISTEN-ING TO?

SO YOU LIKE TO LISTEN TO THE NEWS, HUH?

UH-HUH!

...

...AND THOSE JEWEL THIEVES ON THE RUN!!

HAVE THE THIEVES BEEN ARRESTED?

BUT I'M SURE THEY'LL GET CAUGHT SOON!

THEY'RE STILL SOMEWHERE IN THE GUNMA AREA!

LOOK, A POLICE CHECK-POINT!

UM... SURE...

YOUR LICENSE, PLEASE.

SKREE

DETECTIVE YAMA-MURA!!

WHY, IT'S CONAN!

AFTER THEY ROBBED A JEWELRY STORE IN GUNMA, THEY ABANDONED THEIR GETAWAY CAR IN THE MOUNTAINS AND DISAPPEARED.

BUT ONE OF THEM IS INJURED, SO THEY CAN'T HAVE GOTTEN FAR.

IT WAS A GANG OF THREE, ALL IN SKI MASKS.

THAT'S RIGHT.

ARE YOU TRYING TO CATCH THOSE JEWEL THIEVES?

IT WENT OFF WITH A BIG *BANG*, JUST LIKE IN A COP SHOW!!

THAT'S RIGHT!! MY WARNING SHOT ACCIDENTALLY HIT ONE OF THE ROBBERS IN THE THIGH!

IN-JURED?

YOU BET I HAVE!

HAVE I?

YOU HAVEN'T SEEN ANY SUSPICIOUS CHARACTERS RIDING AROUND IN A CAR THAT'S NOT THEIRS, HAVE YOU?

...WE SUSPECT THE THIEVES EITHER HAD A SECOND CAR READY OR STOLE A VEHICLE. EITHER WAY, THEY'RE ON THE RUN!

ANY-WAY...

A HEM!!

MY CAR GOT A FLAT TIRE IN THE MOUNTAINS. THIS YOUNG COUPLE WAS KIND ENOUGH TO GIVE US A LIFT!

OH, I SEE.

HUH?

ME AND DOC AGASA!

I CALLED MY MECHANIC. THEY'LL DROP BY IN THE MORNING AND PICK UP THE CAR, SO I LEFT MY KEYS INSIDE.

BUT WHAT ABOUT YOUR CAR?

DON'T WORRY ABOUT US! GO CHECK TO MAKE SURE THE CAR IS SAFE!

THAT *IS* A POSSIBILITY...

IT'LL BE EASY TO FIND! IT'S BRIGHT YELLOW!

WHAT IF THOSE ROBBERS STEAL YOUR CAR?

BUT THAT'S VERY DANGEROUS!

WHAT?

HUH?

CAN WE GO NOW, DETECTIVE?

IT'S JUST YOUR IMAGINATION.

YOU KNOW, I'M SURE I'VE HEARD YOUR VOICES SOMEWHERE BEFORE...

SORRY, MA'AM.

I HAVEN'T BEEN SHOT!

OKAY, LOOK!

DO I LOOK SUSPI-CIOUS TO YOU?

UM... I'M SORRY, BUT COULD YOU PLEASE TAKE THAT JACKET OFF YOUR LAP?

HAVE A SAFE TRIP!!

VROOOM

YAWN...

BRRNG

BRRNG

BRRNG

BRRNG

BRRNG

GUNMA POLICE?

WHAT?

AGASA RESI-DENCE...

OF COURSE.

PLEASE TELL HIM TO COME TO THE GUNMA POLICE STATION TOMORROW FOR HIS CAR.

...BUT WE'RE AFRAID THE ROBBERS MIGHT USE IT TO ESCAPE, SO WE'VE DECIDED TO TOW IT.

ACCORDING TO MR. AGASA, HIS MECHANIC WAS PLANNING TO PICK UP HIS CAR IN THE MORNING...

WHAT ARE THEY DOING IN GUNMA AT THIS HOUR?

CHAK

...OFF ON ANOTHER ABSURD CASE.

I BET JIMMY DRAGGED POOR DR. AGASA...

JIMMY'S SPARE TRACKING GLASSES...

I JUST DON'T SEE THE FUN IN BEING A DETECTIVE.

HE'S ALWAYS STICKING HIS NOSE WHERE IT DOESN'T BELONG! DOES HE EVER SLEEP?

YAWN...

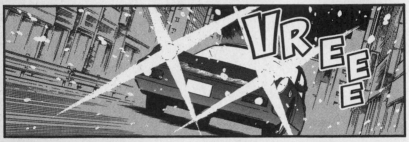

YOU CAN TELL THE BOSS THAT.

SAME PLACE. THE LOCKERS IN THE LOWEST LEVEL OF KENBASHI STATION.

AT 4 A.M., AN HOUR FROM NOW.

YEAH, YOU HEARD ME. I'LL BE PICKING UP THE GOODS AHEAD OF SCHEDULE.

I THINK HE MIGHT CHICKEN OUT AND CALL THE COPS.

MAKE SURE WE'VE GOT PLENTY OF *ARMED BACKUP.*

YEAH, THAT'S RIGHT.

...BY BURYING HIS CORPSE AT THE CONSTRUCTION SITE AT THE STATION.

WE WERE GONNA END THINGS WITH HIM AFTER THIS DEAL ANYWAY...

KENBASHI STATION, LIKE YOU SAID.

VROOM

WE'RE ALMOST THERE, YOU TWO.

YEAH...

HEY, JIMMY. YOU STILL WANT TO DO THIS?

ER... MY HOUSE IS NEARBY.

BUT ISN'T IT STILL UNDER CONSTRUCTION? YOU CAN'T CATCH A TRAIN THERE.

SORRY!

I DON'T LIKE PEOPLE WHISPERING IN MY CAR.

...BUT THERE'S SOMETHING I'VE GOT TO TAKE CARE OF FIRST.

BSH

I'LL GET RID OF IT!

VWEEEN

SORRY, SORRY...

YOU IDIOT! DIDN'T I TELL YOU NOT TO SMOKE?

OH, RIGHT.

OH...

USE THE ASH-TRAY!

HEY, DON'T JUST TOSS IT OUT THE WINDOW!

POK

CHING

HE DIDN'T MEAN TO.

NO MATTER HOW RICH YOU MAY BE, YOU SHOULDN'T TREAT GOOD MONEY THIS WAY!

OH MY! THESE COINS ARE COVERED IN CIGARETTE BUTTS!!

THESE TWO ARE THE JEWEL THIEVES.

THE REAL OWNER IS A NONSMOKER WHO KEEPS LOOSE CHANGE IN THE ASHTRAY TO PAY TOLLS.

THEY MUST'VE STOLEN THIS CAR FROM SOMEONE AFTER STASHING THEIR GETAWAY CAR IN THE MOUNTAINS.

WHAT?

WH...

THERE'S MORE PROOF THAT THIS CAR DOESN'T BELONG TO HIM.

DON'T BE SILLY, LITTLE BOY! THOSE COINS ARE JUST A LITTLE TRICK I PLAYED ON HIM TO MAKE HIM STOP SMOKING!

THIS GUY THREW HIS CIGARETTE BUTTS IN THE ASHTRAY BEFORE REALIZING IT WAS FULL OF COINS. EVEN THEN, HE KEPT DOING IT...

...UNTIL HE PICKED US UP.

I WONDERED WHY HE MADE US GET INTO THE CAR ON THE RIGHT SIDE, WHEN THE LEFT-HAND DOORS WERE RIGHT IN FRONT OF US.

BUT AFTER WHAT DETECTIVE YAMAMURA SAID, IT'S OBVIOUS.

HE FORGOT THAT THE SWITCHES ARE ON THE OPPOSITE SIDES IN AMERICAN CARS!

AND WHEN HE TRIED TO TURN, HE SWITCHED ON THE WINDSHIELD WIPERS INSTEAD OF THE TURN SIGNAL!

...AND HAD TROUBLE SHIFTING GEARS WITH HIS RIGHT HAND!

HE'S NOT USED TO LEFT-HAND DRIVING. HE KEEPS VEERING TOO CLOSE TO THE CENTER OF THE ROAD. WHEN HE PUT THE CAR IN REVERSE, HE AUTOMATICALLY TURNED TO THE LEFT...

BUT WHY WOULD THEY PICK US UP?

BECAUSE THEY'RE **SMART.** ORDINARY THIEVES WOULDN'T STOP TO PICK UP HITCH-HIKERS...

HE OR SHE PROBABLY HID IN THE TRUNK TO GET PAST THE POLICE CHECK-POINT.

...TO COVER UP BLOOD SPILLED BY YOUR PARTNER, WHO WAS SITTING THERE BEFORE!

THE LADY IS SITTING IN THAT SEAT...

THE ONLY PEOPLE WHO'D PICK UP HITCH-HIKERS IN A STOLEN CAR...

THAT'S HOW I REALIZED WHO THEY WERE!

THE POLICE WOULDN'T SUS-PECT A GROUP THAT INCLUDED AN OLD MAN AND A LITTLE BOY. WE'D LOOK LIKE A FAMILY ON AN OUTING!

...BUT THESE TWO REALIZED WE COULD HELP THEM GET PAST THE CHECK-POINT!

...WOULD BE THOSE JEWEL THIEVES ON THE LOOSE!!!

Hello, Aoyama here.

The 2002 World Cup, held in South Korea and Japan, has finally arrived!

Conan's looking forward to the World Cup!

Richard loves to drink One Cup*!

Rachel's cup size is... ♥

And I'll be eating Cup Noodle for dinner again tonight. Funny, isn't it?

*A cheap brand of sake commonly available at Japanese convenience stores.

Gosho Aoyama's
Mystery Library

37

HENRY JACKSON

Once a month, a group called the "Black Widowers" gathers at the restaurant Milano in New York. This unique group includes a lawyer, a writer, an organic chemist, a painter, a mathematician and a code breaker, all of whom pool their talents to solve a strange mystery presented by that month's dinner guest. And the hidden genius of the group is the old waiter, Henry Jackson!

This detective, created by writer Isaac Asimov, is over 60 years old, yet his face is unlined. He is always reserved, serving dishes quickly and precisely, almost like a robot. But when the Black Widowers, each a top specialist in his field, are puzzled over how to solve their guest's problem, Henry comes up with the solution almost immediately! I'd love to attend this gathering and have Henry solve the mystery of why my stomach has started to expand lately... heh.

I recommend "The Acquisitive Chuckle."

Ranma½ Returns!
REMASTERED AND BETTER THAN EVER!

One day, teenaged martial artist Ranma Saotome went on a training mission with his father and ended up taking a dive into some cursed springs at a legendary training ground in China. Now, every time he's splashed with cold water, he changes into a girl. His father, Genma, changes into a panda! What's a half-guy, half-girl to do?

Find out what fueled the worldwide manga boom in beloved creator Rumiko Takahashi's (*Inuyasha, Urusei Yatsura, RIN-NE*) smash-hit of martial arts mayhem!

Story and Art by Rumiko Takahashi

Hey! You're Reading in the Wrong Direction!

This is the **end** of this graphic novel!

To properly enjoy this VIZ graphic novel, please turn it around and begin reading from **right to left.** Unlike English, Japanese is read right to left, so Japanese comics are read in reverse order from the way English comics are typically read.

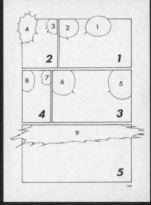

Follow the action this way

This book has been printed in the original Japanese format in order to preserve the orientation of the original artwork. Have fun with it!